Edexcel
advancing learning, changing lives

Mechanics 3

Edexcel AS and A-level Modular Mathematics

Susan Hooker
Mick Jennings
Jean Littlewood
Bronwen Moran
Laurence Pateman

Contents

About this book

This book is designed to provide you with the best preparation possible for your Edexcel M3 unit examination:

- The LiveText CD-ROM in the back of the book contains even more resources to support you through the unit.

> Brief chapter overview and 'links' to underline the importance of mathematics: to the real world, to your study of further units and to your career

Finding your way around the book

> Detailed contents list shows which parts of the M3 specification are covered in each section

> Every few chapters, a review exercise helps you consolidate your learning

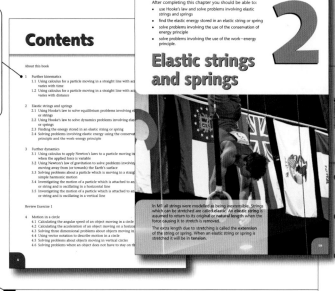

> Each section begins with a statement of what is covered in the section

> Concise learning points

> Step-by-step worked examples

> Past examination questions are marked 'E'

> Each section ends with an exercise – the questions are carefully graded so they increase in difficulty and gradually bring you up to standard

> Each chapter has a different colour scheme, to help you find the right chapter quickly

> Each chapter ends with a mixed exercise and a summary of key points.

> At the end of the book there is an examination-style paper.

LiveText software

The LiveText software gives you additional resources: Solutionbank and Exam café. Simply turn the pages of the electronic book to the page you need, and explore!

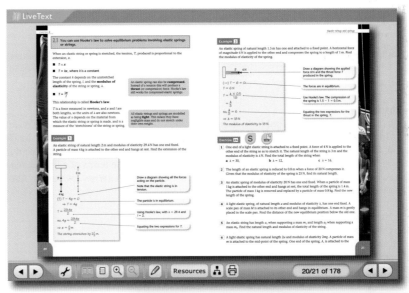

Unique Exam café feature:

- Relax and prepare – revision planner; hints and tips; common mistakes
- Refresh your memory – revision checklist; language of the examination; glossary
- Get the result! – fully worked examination-style paper

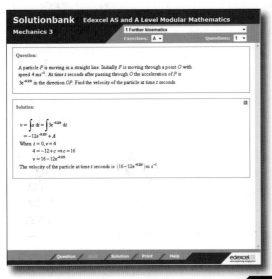

Solutionbank

- Hints and solutions to every question in the textbook
- Solutions and commentary for all review exercises and the practice examination paper

Published by Pearson Education Limited, a company incorporated in England and Wales, having its registered office at 80 Strand, London, WC2R 0RL. Registered company number: 872828

Edexcel is a registered trademark of Edexcel Limited

Text © Susan Hooker, Mick Jennings, Jean Littlewood, Bronwen Moran, Laurence Pateman 2009

16
12

British Library Cataloguing in Publication Data is available from the British Library on request.

ISBN 978 0 435519 18 6

Edited by Harry Smith and Susan Gardner
Typeset by Tech-Set Ltd
Illustrated by Tech-Set Ltd
Cover design by Christopher Howson
Picture research by Chrissie Martin
Cover photo/illustration © Science Photo Library / Laguna Design
Printed in China (CTPS/12)

Acknowledgements
The author and publisher would like to thank the following individuals and organisations for permission to reproduce photographs:

Shutterstock / Chad McDermott p**1**; Shutterstock / Galina Barskaya p**19**; Getty Images / PhotoDisc p**37**; Masterfile / Rommel p**86**; Shutterstock / Mariette Budel p**118**

Every effort has been made to contact copyright holders of material reproduced in this book. Any omissions will be rectified in subsequent printings if notice is given to the publishers.

Disclaimer
This Edexcel publication offers high-quality support for the delivery of Edexcel qualifications.
Edexcel endorsement does not mean that this material is essential to achieve any Edexcel qualification, nor does it mean that this is the only suitable material available to support any Edexcel qualification. No endorsed material will be used verbatim in setting any Edexcel examination/assessment and any resource lists produced by Edexcel shall include this and other appropriate texts.
Copies of official specifications for all Edexcel qualifications may be found on the Edexcel website – www.edexcel.com.

After completing this chapter you should be able to:

- solve problems involving motion in a straight line when acceleration varies with time
- solve problems involving motion in a straight line when acceleration varies with displacement.

Further kinematics

As a diver enters water, the water causes the diver to slow down. The downwards acceleration of the diver decreases with time.

As a rocket leaves the Earth, the force of gravitation varies inversely with the distance of the rocket from the centre of the Earth. The further the rocket travels from the surface of the Earth the weaker the force of gravity.

1.1 You can use calculus for a particle moving in a straight line with acceleration that varies with time.

In M2 you learnt these connections between displacement (x), velocity (v) and acceleration (a) when the acceleration of a particle is varying with time.

■ **To find the velocity from the displacement, you differentiate with respect to time.**
To find the acceleration from the velocity, you differentiate with respect to time.

$$v = \frac{dx}{dt} \text{ and } a = \frac{dv}{dt} = \frac{d^2x}{dt^2}.$$

■ **To obtain the velocity from the acceleration, you integrate with respect to time.**
To obtain the displacement from the velocity, you integrate with respect to time.

$$v = \int a\,dt \text{ and } x = \int v\,dt.$$

These relationships are summarised in the following diagram.

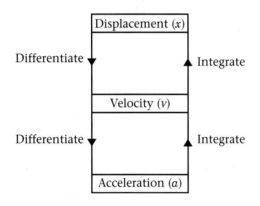

When you integrate, it is important that you remember to include a constant of integration. Many questions include information which enables you to find the value of this constant.

In M3 you will solve problems about the motion of a particle in a straight line using the techniques of integration that you learnt in C4.

Example 1

A particle P starts from rest at a point O and moves along a straight line. At time t seconds the acceleration, $a\,\text{m s}^{-2}$, of P is given by

$$a = \frac{6}{(t+2)^2}, \ t \geq 0.$$

a Find the velocity of P at time t seconds.

b Show that the displacement of P from O when $t = 6$ is $(18 - 12\ln 2)\,\text{m}$.

a $a = 6(t + 2)^{-2}$

To integrate, write $\dfrac{1}{(t + 2)^2}$ as $(t + 2)^{-2}$.

$$v = \int a\,dt = \int 6(t + 2)^{-2}\,dt = \frac{6(t + 2)^{-1}}{-1} + A$$

$$= A - \frac{6}{t + 2}$$

You find the velocity by integrating the acceleration with respect to time. It is important to include a constant of integration. The question includes information which enables you to find this constant.

When $t = 0$, $v = 0$

$$0 = A - \frac{6}{2} \Rightarrow A = 3$$

$$v = 3 - \frac{6}{t + 2}$$

P starts from rest. This means that $v = 0$ when $t = 0$. This pair of values enables you to find the constant of integration.

The velocity of P at time t seconds is

$$\left(3 - \frac{6}{t + 2}\right) \text{m s}^{-1}.$$

b Let the displacement of P from O at time t seconds be s metres.

$$s = \int v\,dt = \int \left(3 - \frac{6}{t + 2}\right) dt$$

$$= 3t - 6\ln(t + 2) + B$$

You find the displacement by integrating the velocity with respect to time. It is important to include a constant of integration.

When $t = 0$, $s = 0$

$$0 = -6\ln 2 + B \Rightarrow B = 6\ln 2$$

$$s = 3t - 6\ln(t + 2) + 6\ln 2$$

When $t = 6$

$$s = 18 - 6\ln 8 + 6\ln 2$$

As P starts at O, $s = 0$ when $t = 0$. This enables you to find the second constant of integration.

$$= 18 - 6\ln\left(\frac{8}{2}\right) = 18 - 6\ln 4 = 18 - 12\ln 2$$

The displacement of P from O when $t = 6$ is $(18 - 12\ln 2)$ m, as required.

You use the laws of logarithms to simplify your answer into the form asked for in the question. This can be done in more than one way. The working shown here uses

$$\ln 8 - \ln 2 = \ln\left(\frac{8}{2}\right) = \ln 4$$

and

$$\ln 4 = \ln 2^2 = 2\ln 2.$$

Example 2

A particle P is moving along the x-axis. At time $t = 0$, the particle is at the origin O and is moving with speed $2 \, \text{m s}^{-1}$ in the direction Ox. At time t seconds, where $t \geq 0$, the acceleration of P is $4e^{-0.5t} \, \text{m s}^{-2}$ directed away from O.

a Find the velocity of P at time t seconds.

b Show that the speed of P cannot exceed $10 \, \text{m s}^{-1}$.

c Sketch a speed–time graph to illustrate the motion of P.

a $a = 4e^{-0.5t}$

Let the velocity of P at time t seconds be $v \, \text{m s}^{-1}$.

$$v = \int a \, dt = \int 4e^{-0.5t} \, dt$$

$$= -8e^{-0.5t} + C$$

When $t = 0$, $v = 2$

$$2 = -8 + C \Rightarrow C = 10$$

$$v = 10 - 8e^{-0.5t}$$

The velocity of P at time t seconds is $(10 - 8e^{-0.5t}) \, \text{m s}^{-1}$.

b For all x, $e^x > 0$ and so for all t, $8e^{-0.5t} > 0$.

It follows that $10 - 8e^{-0.5t} < 10$ for all t.

Hence, the speed of P cannot exceed $10 \, \text{m s}^{-1}$.

c

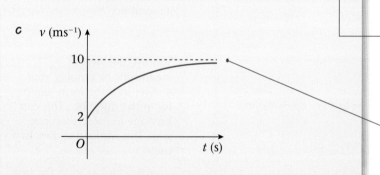

> Using the rule
> $$\int e^{kt} \, dt = \frac{1}{k} e^{kt} + C.$$
> Remember to include a constant of integration.

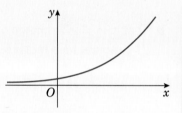

> This sketch of $y = e^x$ illustrates that $e^x > 0$, for all real values of x; both positive and negative.

> 10 minus a positive number must be less than 10.

> The curve approaches the line $v = 10$ but does not reach it. The line is an asymptote to the curve. The speed $10 \, \text{m s}^{-1}$ is the **terminal speed** of P.

Example 3

A particle P is moving along the x-axis. At time t seconds, the velocity of P is $v\,\text{m}\,\text{s}^{-1}$, where $v = 4\sin(2\pi t)$. When $t = 0$, P is at O. Find

a the magnitude of the acceleration of P when $t = \frac{2}{3}$,

b the greatest distance from O attained by P during the motion.

a Let the acceleration of P at time t seconds be $a\,\text{m}\,\text{s}^{-2}$.

$$a = \frac{dv}{dt} = 8\pi\cos(2\pi t)$$

When $t = \frac{2}{3}$

$$a = 8\pi\cos\left(\frac{4\pi}{3}\right) = 8\pi \times -\frac{1}{2} = -4\pi$$

The magnitude of the acceleration of P when $t = \frac{2}{3}$ is $4\pi\,\text{m}\,\text{s}^{-2}$.

> You find the acceleration by differentiating the velocity with respect to time.
>
> $\frac{d}{dt}(\sin kt) = k\cos kt$.
>
> Here $k = 2\pi$.

> In kinematics, it is assumed that angles are measured in radians, unless otherwise stated, and $\cos\left(\frac{4\pi}{3}\right) = -\frac{1}{2}$.

b Let the displacement of P at time t seconds be x metres.

$$x = \int v\,dt = -\frac{4}{2\pi}\cos(2\pi t) + C$$

$$= -\frac{2}{\pi}\cos(2\pi t) + C$$

When $t = 0$, $x = 0$

$$0 = -\frac{2}{\pi} + C \Rightarrow C = \frac{2}{\pi}$$

$$x = \frac{2}{\pi}(1 - \cos(2\pi t))$$

The greatest value of x occurs when $\cos(2\pi t) = -1$

The greatest value of x is $\frac{2}{\pi}(1 - (-1)) = \frac{4}{\pi}$

The greatest distance from O attained by P during the motion is $\frac{4}{\pi}\,\text{m}$.

> You find the displacement by integrating the velocity with respect to time. Use the initial condition in the question to find the constant of integration.

> When $t = 0$, $\cos(2\pi t) = \cos 0 = 1$.

> The cosine of any function varies between $+1$ and -1 and so $1 - \cos(2\pi t)$ varies between 0 and 2. Its greatest value is therefore 2. You do not need to use calculus in this part of the question.

Example **4**

A particle P is moving along the x-axis. Initially P is at the origin O. At time t seconds (where $t \geqslant 0$) the velocity, $v\,\mathrm{m\,s^{-1}}$, of P is given by $v = te^{-\frac{t}{4}}$. Find the distance of P from O when the acceleration of P is zero.

$$a = \frac{dv}{dt} = e^{-\frac{t}{4}} - \frac{1}{4}te^{-\frac{t}{4}} = e^{-\frac{t}{4}}\left(1 - \frac{1}{4}t\right)$$

When $a = 0$, as $e^{-\frac{t}{4}} \neq 0$,

$$1 - \frac{1}{4}t = 0 \Rightarrow t = 4$$

$$x = \int v\,dt = \int te^{-\frac{t}{4}}\,dt$$

$$= -4te^{-\frac{t}{4}} + \int 4e^{-\frac{t}{4}}\,dt$$

$$= -4te^{-\frac{t}{4}} - 16e^{-\frac{t}{4}} + A$$

$$= A - e^{-\frac{t}{4}}(4t + 16)$$

When $t = 0$, $x = 0$

$$0 = A - 16 \Rightarrow A = 16$$

Hence

$$x = 16 - e^{-\frac{t}{4}}(4t + 16)$$

When $t = 4$

$$x = 16 - e^{-1}(4 \times 4 + 16) = 16(1 - 2e^{-1})$$

When the acceleration of P is zero, $OP = 16(1 - 2e^{-1})$ m.

The first step is to find the value of t for which the acceleration is zero. You find the acceleration by differentiating the velocity using the product rule $\frac{d}{dt}(uv) = v\frac{du}{dt} + u\frac{dv}{dt}$ with $u = t$ and $v = e^{-\frac{t}{4}}$.

You find the displacement by integrating the velocity with respect to time. You need to use integration by parts $\int u\frac{dv}{dt}\,dt = uv - \int v\frac{du}{dt}\,dt$ with $u = t$ and $\frac{dv}{dt} = e^{-\frac{t}{4}}$.

You use the information that P is initially at the origin to find the value of the constant of integration A.

Substitute $t = 4$ into your expression for the displacement.

Example 5

A particle is moving along the x-axis. At time t seconds the velocity of P is $v\,\text{m s}^{-1}$ in the direction of x increasing, where

$$v = \begin{cases} 2t, & 0 \leqslant t \leqslant 2 \\ 2 + \dfrac{4}{t}, & t > 2 \end{cases}$$

When $t = 0$, P is at the origin O.

a Sketch a velocity–time graph to illustrate the motion of P in the interval $0 \leqslant t \leqslant 5$.

b Find the distance of P from O when $t = 5$.

a

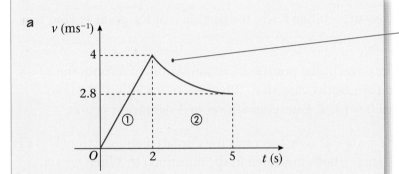

For $v = 2t$, when $t = 0$,
$v = 0$ and when $t = 2$, $v = 4$.
The graph is the line segment
joining $(0, 0)$ to $(2, 4)$.

For $v = 2 + \dfrac{4}{t}$, when $t = 2$,

$v = 4$ and when $t = 5$,
$v = 2.8$. The graph is part of
a hyperbola joining $(2, 4)$ to
$(5, 2.8)$.

b The distance moved in the first two seconds is represented by the area labelled ①.

Let this area be A_1.

The distance moved by P
is represented by the area
between the graph and the
t-axis.

$$A_1 = \tfrac{1}{2} \times 2 \times 4 = 4$$

The area labelled ① can be
found using the formula for
the area of a triangle
$\tfrac{1}{2} \times$ base $\times$ height.

The distance travelled in the next three seconds is represented by the area labelled ②.

Let this area be A_2.

$$A_2 = \int_2^5 \left(2 + \frac{4}{t}\right) dt$$

$$= \left[2t + 4\ln t\right]_2^5$$

$$= (10 + 4\ln 5) - (4 + 4\ln 2)$$

$$= 6 + 4(\ln 5 - \ln 2) = 6 + 4\ln\tfrac{5}{2}$$

The area labelled ② in the
diagram can be found by
definite integration.

Integrate the function $2 + \dfrac{4}{t}$

between the limits $t = 2$ and
$t = 5$

The distance of P from O when $t = 5$ is

$$\left(4 + 6 + 4\ln\tfrac{5}{2}\right) \text{m} = \left(10 + 4\ln\tfrac{5}{2}\right) \text{m}.$$

Exercise **1A**

1 A particle P is moving in a straight line. Initially P is moving through a point O with speed $4\,\mathrm{m\,s^{-1}}$. At time t seconds after passing through O the acceleration of P is $3\mathrm{e}^{-0.25t}\,\mathrm{m\,s^{-2}}$ in the direction OP. Find the velocity of the particle at time t seconds.

2 A particle P is moving along the x-axis in the direction of x increasing. At time t seconds, the velocity of P is $(t\sin t)\,\mathrm{m\,s^{-1}}$. When $t = 0$, P is at the origin. Show that when $t = \frac{\pi}{2}$, P is 1 metre from O.

3 At time t seconds the velocity, $v\,\mathrm{m\,s^{-1}}$, of a particle moving in a straight line is given by

$$v = \frac{4}{3 + 2t},\ t \geqslant 0.$$

When $t = 0$, the particle is at a point A. When $t = 3$, the particle is at the point B. Find the distance between A and B.

4 A particle P is moving along the x-axis in the positive direction. At time t seconds the acceleration of P is $4\mathrm{e}^{\frac{1}{2}t}\,\mathrm{m\,s^{-2}}$ in the positive direction. When $t = 0$, P is at rest. Find the distance P moves in the interval $0 \leqslant t \leqslant 2$. Give your answer to 3 significant figures.

5 A particle P is moving along the x-axis. At time t seconds the displacement of P from O is x m and the velocity of P is $(4\cos 3t)\,\mathrm{m\,s^{-1}}$, both measured in the direction Ox. When $t = 0$ the particle P is at the origin O. Find

a the magnitude of the acceleration when $t = \frac{\pi}{12}$,

b x in terms of t,

c the smallest positive value of t for which P is at O.

6 A particle P is moving along a straight line. Initially P is at rest. At time t seconds P has velocity $v\,\mathrm{m\,s^{-1}}$ and acceleration $a\,\mathrm{m\,s^{-2}}$ where

$$a = \frac{6t}{(2 + t^2)^2},\ t \geqslant 0.$$

Find v in terms of t.

7 A particle P is moving along the x-axis. At time t seconds the velocity of P is $v\,\mathrm{m\,s^{-1}}$ in the direction of x increasing, where

$$v = \begin{cases} 4, & 0 \leqslant t \leqslant 3 \\ 5 - \dfrac{3}{t}, & 3 < t \leqslant 6 \end{cases}$$

When $t = 0$, P is at the origin O.

a Sketch a velocity–time graph to illustrate the motion of P in the interval $0 \leqslant t \leqslant 6$.

b Find the distance of P from O when $t = 6$.

8 A particle P is moving in a straight line with acceleration $\left(\sin\frac{1}{2}t\right)\,\mathrm{m\,s^{-2}}$ at time t seconds, $t \geqslant 0$. The particle is initially at rest at a point O. Find

a the speed of P when $t = 2\pi$,

b the distance of P from O when $t = \frac{\pi}{2}$.

9 A particle P is moving along the x-axis. At time t seconds P has velocity $v\,\text{m s}^{-1}$ in the direction x increasing and an acceleration of magnitude $4\text{e}^{0.2t}\,\text{m s}^{-2}$ in the direction x decreasing. When $t = 0$, P is moving through the origin with velocity $20\,\text{m s}^{-1}$ in the direction x increasing. Find

a v in terms of t,

b the maximum value of x attained by P during its motion.

10 A car is travelling along a straight road. As it passes a sign S, the driver applies the brakes. The car is modelled as a particle. At time t seconds the car is $x\,\text{m}$ from S and its velocity, $v\,\text{m s}^{-1}$, is modelled by the equation $v = \dfrac{3200}{c + dt}$, where c and d are constants.

Given that when $t = 0$, the speed of the car is $40\,\text{m s}^{-1}$ and its deceleration is $0.5\,\text{m s}^{-2}$, find

a the value of c and the value of d,

b x in terms of t.

11 A particle P is moving along a straight line. When $t = 0$, P is passing through a point A. At time t seconds after passing through A the velocity, $v\,\text{m s}^{-1}$, of P is given by

$$v = \text{e}^{2t} - 11\text{e}^{t} + 15t.$$

Find

a the values of t for which the acceleration is zero,

b the distance of P from A when $t = \ln 3$.

12 A particle P moves along a straight line. At time t seconds (where $t \geq 0$) the velocity of P is $[2t + \ln(t + 2)]\,\text{m s}^{-1}$. Find

a the value of t for which the acceleration has magnitude $2.2\,\text{m s}^{-2}$,

b the distance moved by P in the interval $1 \leq t \leq 4$.

1.2 You can use calculus for a particle moving in a straight line with acceleration that varies with distance.

When the acceleration of a particle is varying with time, the displacement (x), velocity (v) and acceleration (a) are connected by the relationships

$$a = \frac{\text{d}v}{\text{d}t} = \frac{\text{d}^2x}{\text{d}t^2}$$

Using the chain rule for differentiation

$$a = \frac{\text{d}v}{\text{d}t} = \frac{\text{d}v}{\text{d}x} \times \frac{\text{d}x}{\text{d}t}$$

As $v = \dfrac{\text{d}x}{\text{d}t}$

$$a = \frac{\text{d}v}{\text{d}x} \times v = v\frac{\text{d}v}{\text{d}x} \qquad \qquad ①$$

Also, if you differentiate $\frac{1}{2}v^2$ implicitly with respect to x, you obtain

$$\frac{\mathrm{d}}{\mathrm{d}x}\left(\frac{1}{2}v^2\right) = \frac{1}{2} \times 2v \times \frac{\mathrm{d}v}{\mathrm{d}x} = v\frac{\mathrm{d}v}{\mathrm{d}x} \qquad ②$$

Combining results ① and ②, you obtain

■ $a = v\dfrac{\mathrm{d}v}{\mathrm{d}x} = \dfrac{\mathrm{d}}{\mathrm{d}x}\left(\dfrac{1}{2}v^2\right)$

With these alternative forms for acceleration you can solve problems where the acceleration of a particle varies with distance.

For example, if you have an equation of the form

$$a = \mathrm{f}(x)$$

you can write this as

$$\frac{\mathrm{d}}{\mathrm{d}x}\left(\frac{1}{2}v^2\right) = \mathrm{f}(x)$$

> When you integrate, it is important that you remember to include a constant of integration. Many questions include information which enables you to find the value of this constant.

Integrating both sides of the equation with respect to x,

$$\frac{1}{2}v^2 = \int \mathrm{f}(x)\,\mathrm{d}x$$

Example 6

A particle P is moving on the x-axis in the direction of x increasing. When the displacement of P from the origin O is x m and its speed is $v\,\mathrm{m\,s^{-1}}$, the acceleration of P is $2x\,\mathrm{m\,s^{-1}}$. When P is at O, its speed is $6\,\mathrm{m\,s^{-1}}$. Find v in terms of x.

$a = 2x$

$\dfrac{d}{dx}\left(\dfrac{1}{2}v^2\right) = 2x$

$\dfrac{1}{2}v^2 = \int 2x\,dx$

$\quad = x^2 + C$

When $x = 0,\ v = 6$

$\dfrac{1}{2}36 = 0 + C \Rightarrow C = 18$

$\dfrac{1}{2}v^2 = x^2 + 18$

$v^2 = 2x^2 + 36$

$v = \sqrt{(2x^2 + 36)}$

> You use $a = \dfrac{\mathrm{d}}{\mathrm{d}x}\left(\dfrac{1}{2}v^2\right)$.

> You integrate both sides of the equation with respect to x. As integration is the inverse process of differentiation,
> $$\int\frac{\mathrm{d}}{\mathrm{d}x}\left(\frac{1}{2}v^2\right)\mathrm{d}x = \frac{1}{2}v^2.$$

> You multiply by 2 throughout the equation and make v the subject of the formula.

> As the question tells you that P is moving in the direction of x-increasing, you do not need to consider the negative square root.

Example 7

A particle P is moving along a straight line. The acceleration of P, when it has displacement x m from a fixed point O on the line and velocity v m s^{-1}, is of magnitude $4x$ m s^{-2} and is directed towards O. At $x = 0$, $v = 20$. Find the values of x for which P is instantaneously at rest.

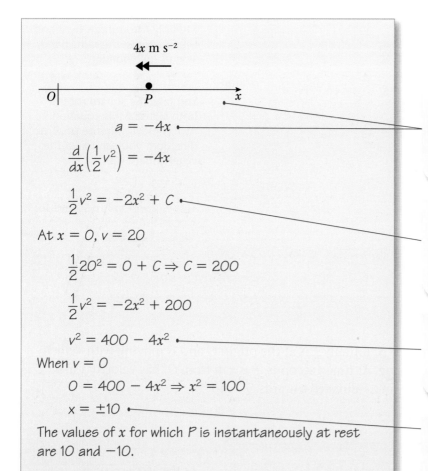

$a = -4x$

As its acceleration is towards O, when P has positive displacement, the acceleration is in the direction of x decreasing, so the acceleration is negative.

$$\frac{d}{dx}\left(\frac{1}{2}v^2\right) = -4x$$

$$\frac{1}{2}v^2 = -2x^2 + C$$

When integrating, you must remember to include a constant of integration. In this question the information that at $x = 0$, $v = 20$ enables you to evaluate the constant.

At $x = 0$, $v = 20$

$$\frac{1}{2}20^2 = 0 + C \Rightarrow C = 200$$

$$\frac{1}{2}v^2 = -2x^2 + 200$$

$$v^2 = 400 - 4x^2$$

The particle is instantaneously at rest when $v = 0$. You substitute $v = 0$ into this expression and solve the resulting equation for x.

When $v = 0$

$$0 = 400 - 4x^2 \Rightarrow x^2 = 100$$

$$x = \pm 10$$

The values of x for which P is instantaneously at rest are 10 and -10.

There are two points at which $v = 0$. The particle reverses direction at these points and will oscillate between them.

Example 8

A particle P is moving along the positive x-axis in the direction of x increasing. When $OP = x$ m, the velocity of P is v m s^{-1} and the acceleration of P is $\left(\dfrac{54}{x^3} - \dfrac{18}{x^5}\right)$ m s^{-2} where $x \geqslant 1$.

Given that $v = 6$ at $x = 1$, find v in terms of x.

$$a = \frac{54}{x^3} - \frac{18}{x^5}$$

$$\frac{d}{dx}\left(\frac{1}{2}v^2\right) = \frac{54}{x^3} - \frac{18}{x^5}$$

$$= 54x^{-3} - 18x^{-5}$$

You integrate both sides of this equation with respect to x using $\int \dfrac{d}{dx}\left(\dfrac{1}{2}v^2\right) dx = \dfrac{1}{2}v^2$ and $\int x^n \, dx = \dfrac{x^{n+1}}{n+1}$.
Remember to include a constant of integration.

$$\frac{1}{2}v^2 = \frac{54x^{-2}}{-2} - \frac{18x^{-4}}{-4} + C$$

$$= C - \frac{27}{x^2} + \frac{9}{2x^4}$$

At $x = 1$, $v = 6$

$$18 = C - 27 + \frac{9}{2} \Rightarrow C = \frac{81}{2}$$

> Multiply throughout by 2 and then factorise the right hand side of the equation.

$$\frac{1}{2}v^2 = \frac{81}{2} - \frac{27}{x^2} + \frac{9}{2x^4}$$

$$v^2 = 81 - \frac{54}{x^2} + \frac{9}{x^4} = \left(9 - \frac{3}{x^2}\right)^2$$

$$v = 9 - \frac{3}{x^2}$$

> You take the square root of both sides of this equation. As P is moving in the positive direction, you can reject the other square root
>
> $v = -\left(9 - \frac{3}{x^2}\right)$.
>
> This expression is negative for $x \geqslant 1$.

Example 9

A particle P is moving along the x-axis. Initially P is at the origin O and is moving with velocity $1\,\mathrm{m\,s^{-1}}$ in the direction of x increasing. At time t seconds, P is $x\,\mathrm{m}$ from O, has velocity $v\,\mathrm{m\,s^{-1}}$ and acceleration of magnitude $\frac{1}{2}e^{-x}\,\mathrm{m\,s^{-2}}$ directed towards O. Find

a v in terms of x,

b x in terms of t.

a $$a = -\frac{1}{2}e^{-x}$$

> As the acceleration is directed toward O, it is in the direction of x decreasing and is negative.

$$\frac{d}{dx}\left(\frac{1}{2}v^2\right) = -\frac{1}{2}e^{-x}$$

$$\frac{1}{2}v^2 = \frac{1}{2}e^{-x} + A$$

> In this example there are two different constants of integration. The initial conditions given in the question enable you to evaluate both constants.

At $x = 0$, $v = 1$

$$\frac{1}{2} = \frac{1}{2} + A \Rightarrow A = 0$$

$$\frac{1}{2}v^2 = \frac{1}{2}e^{-x}$$

> The question requires you to make v the subject of the formula.

$$v^2 = e^{-x}$$

$$v = e^{-\frac{x}{2}}$$

b

$$v = \frac{dx}{dt} = e^{-\frac{x}{2}}$$

$$\int e^{\frac{x}{2}} dx = \int 1\, dt$$

$$2e^{\frac{x}{2}} = t + B$$

When $t = 0, x = 0$

$$2 = 0 + B \Rightarrow B = 2$$

$$2e^{\frac{x}{2}} = t + 2$$

$$e^{\frac{x}{2}} = \frac{t}{2} + 1$$

$$\frac{x}{2} = \ln\left(\frac{t}{2} + 1\right)$$

$$x = 2\ln\left(\frac{t}{2} + 1\right)$$

This is a separable differential equation. You separate the variables then integrate both sides with respect to t. This method was introduced in C4. You will need to use techniques of integration and differentiation from C1, C2, C3 and C4 as part of your M3 course.

To make x the subject of this formula, you take logarithms on both sides of the equation and use the property that $\ln e^{f(x)} = f(x)$.

Example **10**

A particle P is moving along the positive x-axis. At $OP = x$ m, the velocity of P is $v\,\text{m s}^{-1}$ and the acceleration of P is $\frac{k}{(2x + 3)^2}\,\text{m s}^{-2}$, where k is a constant, directed away from O. At $x = 1, v = 10$ and at $x = 6, v = \sqrt{120}$.

a Find the value of k.

b Show that the speed of P cannot exceed $\sqrt{130}\,\text{m s}^{-1}$.

a

$$a = \frac{k}{(2x + 3)^2}$$

$$\frac{d}{dx}\left(\frac{1}{2}v^2\right) = \frac{k}{(2x + 3)^2}$$

$$\frac{1}{2}v^2 = A - \frac{k}{2(2x + 3)}$$

$$v^2 = B - \frac{k}{2x + 3}$$

At $x = 1, v = 10$

$$100 = B - \frac{k}{5} \quad \text{①}$$

At $x = 6, v = \sqrt{120}$

$$120 = B - \frac{k}{15} \quad \text{②}$$

② − ①

$$20 = -\frac{k}{15} - \left(-\frac{k}{5}\right) = \frac{2k}{15}$$

$$k = 20 \times \frac{15}{2} = 150$$

You integrate both sides of this equation with respect to x. For constants a and b and $n \neq -1$,

$$\int (ax + b)^n\, dx = \frac{1}{(n + 1)a}(ax + b)^{n+1} + C.$$

Multiply this equation throughout by 2. Twice one arbitrary constant is another arbitrary constant.

The conditions given in the question give you a pair of simultaneous equations in B and k. You find k to solve part **a**. You will also need to find B to solve part **b**.

b Substituting $k = 150$ into ①

$$100 = B - \frac{150}{5} \Rightarrow B = 130$$

$$v^2 = 130 - \frac{150}{2x + 3}$$

As x is moving along the positive x-axis $x > 0$, and so both $2x + 3$ and $\frac{150}{2x + 3}$ are positive.

Hence

$$v^2 = 130 - \frac{150}{2x + 3} < 130$$

The speed of P cannot exceed $\sqrt{130}\,\text{m s}^{-1}$. •————

As x increases, the velocity of P approaches $\sqrt{130}\,\text{m s}^{-1}$ in the direction Ox asymptotically. Such a velocity is called a **terminal** or **limiting velocity**.

Exercise **1B**

1. A particle P moves along the x-axis. At time $t = 0$, P passes through the origin O with velocity $5\,\text{m s}^{-1}$ in the direction of x increasing. At time t seconds, the velocity of P is $v\,\text{m s}^{-1}$ and $OP = x$ m. The acceleration of P is $\left(2 + \frac{1}{2}x\right)\text{m s}^{-2}$, measured in the positive x direction. Find v^2 in terms of x.

2. A particle P moves along a straight line. When its displacement from a fixed point O on the line is x m and its velocity is $v\,\text{m s}^{-1}$, the deceleration of P is $4x\,\text{m s}^{-2}$. At $x = 2$, $v = 8$. Find v in terms of x.

3. A particle P is moving along the x-axis in the direction of x increasing. At $OP = x$ m $(x > 0)$, the velocity of P is $v\,\text{m s}^{-1}$ and its acceleration is of magnitude $\frac{4}{x^2}\,\text{m s}^{-2}$ in the direction of x increasing. Given that at $x = 2$, $v = 6$ find the value of x for which P is instantaneously at rest.

4. A particle P moves along a straight line. When its displacement from a fixed point O on the line is x m and its velocity is $v\,\text{m s}^{-1}$, the acceleration of P is of magnitude $25x\,\text{m s}^{-2}$ and is directed towards O. At $x = 0$, $v = 40$. In its motion P is instantaneously at rest at two points A and B. Find the distance between A and B.

5. A particle P is moving along the x-axis. At $OP = x$ m, the velocity of P is $v\,\text{m s}^{-1}$ and its acceleration is of magnitude $kx^2\,\text{m s}^{-2}$, where k is a positive constant, in the direction of x decreasing. At $x = 0$, $v = 16$. The particle is instantaneously at rest at $x = 20$. Find

   a the value of k,

   b the velocity of P when $x = 10$.

6 A particle P is moving along the x-axis in the direction of x increasing. At $OP = x$ m, the velocity of P is v m s^{-1} and its acceleration is of magnitude $8x^3$ m s^{-2} in the direction PO. At $x = 2$, $v = 32$. Find the value of x for which $v = 8$.

7 A particle P is moving along the x-axis. When the displacement of P from the origin O is x m, the velocity of P is v m s^{-1} and its acceleration is $6\sin\frac{x}{3}$ m s^{-2}. At $x = 0$, $v = 4$. Find

a v^2 in terms of x,

b the greatest possible speed of P.

8 A particle P is moving along the x-axis. At $x = 0$, the velocity of P is 2 m s^{-1} in the direction of x increasing. At $OP = x$ m, the velocity of P is v m s^{-1} and its acceleration is $(2 + 3e^{-x})$ m s^{-2}. Find the velocity of P at $x = 3$. Give your answer to 3 significant figures.

9 A particle P moves away from the origin O along the positive x-axis. The acceleration of P is of magnitude $\dfrac{4}{2x + 1}$ m s^{-2}, where $OP = x$ m, directed towards O. Given that the speed of P at O is 4 m s^{-1}, find

a the speed of P at $x = 10$,

b the value of x at which P is instantaneously at rest.

Give your answers to 3 significant figures.

10 A particle P is moving along the positive x-axis. At $OP = x$ m, the velocity of P is v m s^{-1} and its acceleration is $\left(x - \dfrac{4}{x^3}\right)$ m s^{-2}. The particle starts from the position where $x = 1$ with velocity 3 m s^{-1} in the direction of x increasing. Find

a v in terms of x,

b the least speed of P during its motion.

11 A particle P is moving along the x-axis. Initially P is at the origin O moving with velocity 15 m s^{-1} in the direction of x increasing. When the displacement of P from O is x m, its acceleration is of magnitude $\left(10 + \frac{1}{4}x\right)$ m s^{-2} directed towards O. Find the distance P moves before first coming to instantaneous rest.

12 A particle P is moving along the x-axis. At time t seconds, P is x m from O, has velocity v m s^{-1} and acceleration of magnitude $6x^{\frac{1}{3}}$ m s^{-2} in the direction of x increasing. When $t = 0$, $x = 8$ and $v = 12$. Find

a v in terms of x,

b x in terms of t.

Mixed exercise **1C**

1 A particle P moves along a straight line. When the displacement of P from a fixed point on the line is x m, its velocity is v m s^{-1} and its acceleration is of magnitude $\dfrac{6}{x^2}$ m s^{-2} in the direction of x increasing. At $x = 3$, $v = 4$. Find v in terms of x.

2 A particle P is moving along the x-axis. At time t seconds, the displacement of P from the origin O is x m and the velocity of P is $4e^{0.5t}\,\mathrm{m\,s^{-1}}$ in the direction Ox. When $t = 0$, P is at O. Find

  a x in terms of t,

  b the acceleration of P when $t = \ln 9$.

3 A particle is moving along the x-axis. At time $t = 0$, P is passing through the origin O with velocity $8\,\mathrm{m\,s^{-1}}$ in the direction of x increasing. When P is x m from O, its acceleration is $\left(3 + \frac{1}{4}x\right)\mathrm{m\,s^{-2}}$ in the direction of x decreasing.

  Find the positive value of x for which P is instantaneously at rest.

4 A particle P is moving on the x-axis. When P is a distance x metres from the origin O, its acceleration is of magnitude $\dfrac{15}{4x^2}\,\mathrm{m\,s^{-2}}$ in the direction OP. Initially P is at the point where $x = 5$ and is moving toward O with speed $6\,\mathrm{m\,s^{-1}}$.

  Find the value of x where P first comes to rest.

5 A particle P moves along the x-axis in the direction x increasing. At time t seconds, the velocity of P is $v\,\mathrm{m\,s^{-1}}$ and its acceleration is $20te^{-t^2}\,\mathrm{m\,s^{-2}}$. When $t = 0$ the speed of P is $8\,\mathrm{m\,s^{-1}}$. Find

  a v in terms of t,

  b the limiting velocity of P.

6 A particle P moves along a straight line. Initially P is at rest at a point O on the line. At time t seconds, where $t \geqslant 0$, the acceleration of P is $\dfrac{18}{(2t + 3)^3}\,\mathrm{m\,s^{-2}}$ directed away from O.

  Find the value of t for which the speed of P is $0.48\,\mathrm{m\,s^{-1}}$.

7 A particle P is moving along the x-axis. At time t seconds, the velocity of P is $v\,\mathrm{m\,s^{-1}}$ and the acceleration of P is $(3 - x)\,\mathrm{m\,s^{-2}}$ in the direction x increasing. Initially P is at the origin O and is moving with speed $4\,\mathrm{m\,s^{-1}}$ in the direction x increasing. Find

  a v^2 in terms of x,

  b the maximum value of v.

8 A particle P is moving along the x-axis. At time $t = 0$, P passes through the origin O. After t seconds the speed of P is $v\,\mathrm{m\,s^{-1}}$, $OP = x$ metres and the acceleration of P is $\dfrac{x^2(5 - x)}{2}\,\mathrm{m\,s^{-2}}$ in the direction x increasing. At $x = 10$, P is instantaneously at rest. Find

  a an expression for v^2 in terms of x,

  b the speed of P when $t = 0$.

9 A particle P moves away from the origin along the positive x-axis. At time t seconds, the acceleration of P is $\dfrac{20}{5x + 2}\,\mathrm{m\,s^{-2}}$, where $OP = x$ m, directed away from O. Given that the speed of P is $3\,\mathrm{m\,s^{-1}}$ at $x = 0$, find, giving your answers to 3 significant figures,

  a the speed of P at $x = 12$,

  b the value of x when the speed of P is $5\,\mathrm{m\,s^{-1}}$.

10 A car moves along a horizontal straight road. At time t seconds the acceleration of the car is $\dfrac{100}{(2t+5)^2}\,\mathrm{m\,s^{-2}}$ in the direction of motion of the car. When $t = 0$, the car is at rest. Find

   a an expression for v in terms of t,

   b the distance moved by the car in the first 10 seconds of its motion.

11 A particle P is moving in a straight line with acceleration $\cos^2 t\,\mathrm{m\,s^{-2}}$ at time t seconds. The particle is initially at rest at a point O.

   a Find the speed of P when $t = \pi$.

   b Show that the distance of P from O when $t = \dfrac{\pi}{4}$ is $\dfrac{1}{64}(\pi^2 + 8)\,\mathrm{m}$.

12 A particle P is moving along the x-axis. At time t seconds, the velocity of P is $v\,\mathrm{m\,s^{-1}}$ in the direction of x increasing, where

$$v = \begin{cases} \frac{1}{2}t^2, & 0 \leqslant t \leqslant 4 \\ 8e^{4-t}, & t > 4 \end{cases}$$

When $t = 0$, P is at the origin O. Find

   a the acceleration of P when $t = 2.5$,

   b the acceleration of P when $t = 5$,

   c the distance of P from O when $t = 6$.

13 A particle P is moving along the x-axis. When $t = 0$, P is passing through O with velocity $3\,\mathrm{m\,s^{-1}}$ in the direction of x increasing. When $0 \leqslant x \leqslant 4$ the acceleration is of magnitude $\left(4 + \frac{1}{2}x\right)\mathrm{m\,s^{-2}}$ in the direction of x increasing. At $x = 4$, the acceleration of P changes. For $x > 4$, the magnitude of the acceleration remains $\left(4 + \frac{1}{2}x\right)\mathrm{m\,s^{-2}}$ but it is now in the direction of x decreasing.

   a Find the speed of P at $x = 4$.

   b Find the positive value of x for which P is instantaneously at rest. Give your answer to 2 significant figures.

14 A particle P is moving along the x-axis. At time t seconds, P has velocity $v\,\mathrm{m\,s^{-1}}$ in the direction x increasing and an acceleration of magnitude $\dfrac{2t+3}{t+1}\,\mathrm{m\,s^{-2}}$ in the direction x increasing. When $t = 0$, P is at rest at the origin O. Find

   a v in terms of t,

   b the distance of P from O when $t = 2$.

15 A particle P is moving along the x-axis. At time t seconds P is x m from O, has velocity $v\,\mathrm{m\,s^{-1}}$ and acceleration of magnitude $(4x + 6)\,\mathrm{m\,s^{-2}}$ in the direction of x increasing. When $t = 0$, P is passing through O with velocity $3\,\mathrm{m\,s^{-1}}$ in the direction of x increasing. Find

   a v in terms of x,

   b x in terms of t.

Summary of key points

1 Velocity is the rate of change of displacement with time.
   To find the velocity from the displacement, you differentiate
   with respect to time.

2 Acceleration is the rate of change of velocity with time.
   To find the acceleration from the velocity, you differentiate
   with respect to time.

3 To find the velocity from the acceleration, you integrate with
   respect to time.

4 To find the displacement from the velocity, you integrate with
   respect to time.

5 When the acceleration is a function of the displacement you
   can use

$$a = \frac{dv}{dx} = \frac{d}{dx}\left(\frac{1}{2}v^2\right)$$

Using symbols:

$$v = \frac{dx}{dt}$$

$$a = \frac{dv}{dt} = \frac{d^2x}{dt^2}$$

$$v = \int a\, dt$$

$$x = \int v\, dt$$

After completing this chapter you should be able to:

- use Hooke's law and solve problems involving elastic strings and springs
- find the elastic energy stored in an elastic string or spring
- solve problems involving the use of the conservation of energy principle
- solve problems involving the use of the work−energy principle.

Elastic strings and springs

In M1 all strings were modelled as being inextensible. Strings which can be stretched are called **elastic**. An **elastic string** is assumed to return to its original or **natural length** when the force causing it to stretch is removed.

The extra length due to stretching is called the **extension** of the string or spring. When an elastic string or spring is stretched it will be in **tension**.

2.1 You can use Hooke's law to solve equilibrium problems involving elastic springs or strings.

When an elastic string or spring is stretched, the tension, T, produced is proportional to the extension, x.

■ $T \propto x$

■ $T = kx$, where k is a constant

The constant k depends on the unstretched length of the spring, l, and the **modulus of elasticity** of the string or spring, λ.

> An elastic spring can also be **compressed**. Instead of a tension this will produce a **thrust** (or compression) force. Hooke's law still works for compressed elastic springs.

■ $T = \dfrac{\lambda x}{l}$

This relationship is called **Hooke's law**.

T is a force measured in newtons, and x and l are both lengths, so the units of λ are also newtons. The value of λ depends on the material from which the elastic string or spring is made, and is a measure of the 'stretchiness' of the string or spring.

> All elastic strings and springs are modelled as being **light**. This means they have negligible mass and do not stretch under their own weight.

Example 1

An elastic string of natural length 2 m and modulus of elasticity 29.4 N has one end fixed. A particle of mass 4 kg is attached to the other end and hangs at rest. Find the extension of the string.

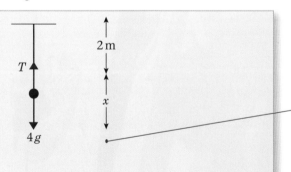

Draw a diagram showing all the forces acting on the particle.

Note that the elastic string is in tension.

$(\uparrow)\ T - 4g = 0$

$\Rightarrow T = 4g$

The particle is in equilibrium.

$T = \dfrac{29.4x}{2}$

Using Hooke's law, with $\lambda = 29.4$ and $l = 2$.

so, $4g = \dfrac{29.4x}{2}$

Equating the two expressions for T.

$\Rightarrow x = \dfrac{8}{3}$ m

The string stretches by $2\frac{2}{3}$ m.

Example 2

An elastic spring of natural length 1.5 m has one end attached to a fixed point. A horizontal force of magnitude 6 N is applied to the other end and compresses the spring to a length of 1 m. Find the modulus of elasticity of the spring.

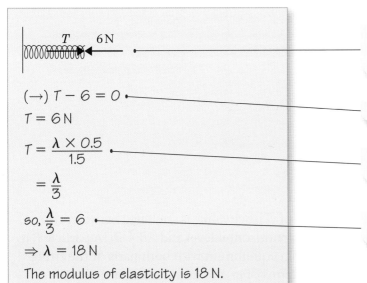

$(\rightarrow) \; T - 6 = 0$

$T = 6 \, \text{N}$

Draw a diagram showing the applied force 6 N and the thrust force T produced in the spring.

The forces are in equilibrium.

$T = \dfrac{\lambda \times 0.5}{1.5}$

$\quad = \dfrac{\lambda}{3}$

Use Hooke's law. The compression of the spring is $1.5 - 1 = 0.5 \, \text{m}$.

so, $\dfrac{\lambda}{3} = 6$

$\Rightarrow \lambda = 18 \, \text{N}$

Equating the two expressions for the thrust in the spring, T.

The modulus of elasticity is 18 N.

Example 3

The elastic springs PQ and QR are joined together at Q to form one long spring. The spring PQ has natural length 1.6 m and modulus of elasticity 20 N. The spring QR has natural length 1.4 m and modulus of elesticity 28 N. The ends, P and R, of the long spring are attached to two fixed points which are 4 m apart, as shown in the diagram.

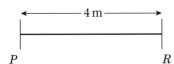

Find the tension in the combined spring.

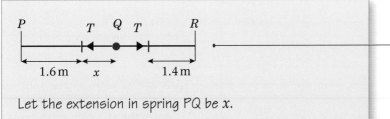

Since Q is at rest the tension in each string must be the same.

Let the extension in spring PQ be x.

The extension in $QR = 1 - x$

Since $PR = 4$ m.

For PQ: $T = \dfrac{20x}{1.6}$

Use Hooke's law.

For QR: $T = \dfrac{28(1 - x)}{1.4}$

$$\text{so, } \frac{20x}{1.6} = \frac{28(1-x)}{1.4}$$ ———— Equate the tensions.

$$\Rightarrow \frac{20x}{1.6} = 32(1-x)$$ ———— Clear fractions.

$$\Rightarrow 52x = 32$$

$$\Rightarrow x = \frac{32}{52} = \frac{8}{13}$$ ———— Solve for x.

$$\text{so, } T = \frac{20}{1.6} \times \frac{8}{13}$$ ———— Substitute.

$$= \frac{100}{13}\text{ N}$$

The tension in the combined spring is $7\frac{9}{13}$ N.

Example 4

An elastic string of natural length $2l$ and modulus of elasticity $4mg$ is stretched between two points A and B. The points A and B are on the same horizontal level and $AB = 2l$. A particle P is attached to the mid-point of the string and hangs in equilibrium with both parts of the string making an angle of $30°$ with the line AB. Find, in terms of m, the mass of the particle.

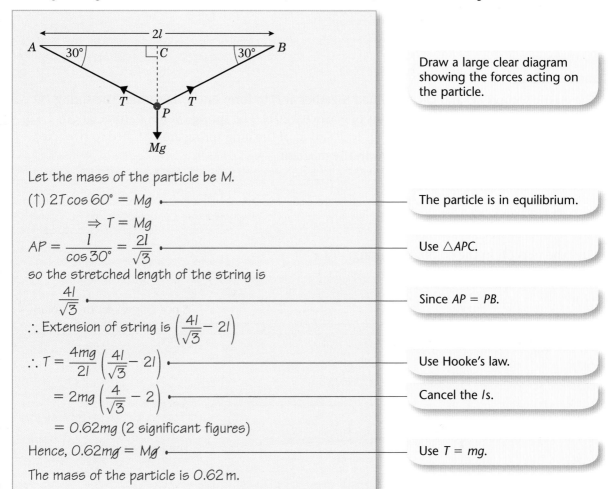

Draw a large clear diagram showing the forces acting on the particle.

Let the mass of the particle be M.

$(\uparrow)\ 2T\cos 60° = Mg$ ———— The particle is in equilibrium.

$$\Rightarrow T = Mg$$

$$AP = \frac{l}{\cos 30°} = \frac{2l}{\sqrt{3}}$$ ———— Use $\triangle APC$.

so the stretched length of the string is

$$\frac{4l}{\sqrt{3}}$$ ———— Since $AP = PB$.

$\therefore$ Extension of string is $\left(\dfrac{4l}{\sqrt{3}} - 2l\right)$

$\therefore T = \dfrac{4mg}{2l}\left(\dfrac{4l}{\sqrt{3}} - 2l\right)$ ———— Use Hooke's law.

$\quad = 2mg\left(\dfrac{4}{\sqrt{3}} - 2\right)$ ———— Cancel the ls.

$\quad = 0.62mg$ (2 significant figures)

Hence, $0.62mg = Mg$ ———— Use $T = mg$.

The mass of the particle is $0.62\,m$.

Example 5

An elastic string has natural length 2 m and modulus of elasticity 98 N. One end of the string is attached to a fixed point O and the other end is attached to a particle P of mass 4 kg. The particle is held in equilibrium by a horizontal force of magnitude 28 N, with OP making an angle θ with the vertical, as shown. Find

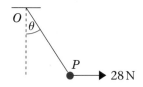

a the value of θ,

b the length OP.

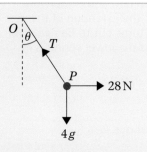

a $(\leftarrow)\ T\sin\theta = 28$ •———————— The particle is in equilibrium.

$(\uparrow)\ T\cos\theta = 4g$

$\tan\theta = \dfrac{28}{4g} = \dfrac{5}{7}$ •———————— Divide the equations to eliminate T.

so, $\theta = 35.5°$

$= 36°$ (2 s.f.)

b $T = \dfrac{28}{\sin\theta}$

so, $\dfrac{28}{\sin\theta} = \dfrac{98x}{2}$ •———————— Use Hooke's law, with x as the extension of the string.

so, $x = \dfrac{4}{7\sin\theta}$ •———————— You can now use your calculator, ensuring that you use an unrounded value for θ, to find x.

$= 0.983...$

$OP = 2 + 0.983... = 2.983...$

$\therefore$ Length of OP is 2.98 m (3 s.f.)

Draw a diagram showing all the forces acting on the particle.

Example 6

Two identical elastic springs PQ and QR have natural length l and modulus of elasticity $2mg$. The springs are joined together at Q. Their other ends, P and R, are attached to fixed points, with P being $4l$ vertically above R. A particle of mass m is attached at Q and hangs at rest in equilibrium. Find the distance of the particle below P.

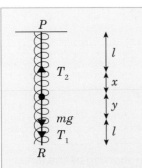

Draw a diagram showing the forces acting on the particle. Note that we have assumed that the lower spring is **stretched** and is therefore in **tension**. If the extension of the lower spring turns out to be negative, then it means the lower spring is in compression.

$l + x + y + l = 4l$ — Since P is $4l$ above R.

$\Rightarrow \qquad\qquad y = (2l - x)$

$(\uparrow) \; T_2 - mg - T_1 = 0$ — Since the mass is in equilibrium.

$\Rightarrow \dfrac{2mgx}{l} = mg + \dfrac{2mg(2l - x)}{l}$ — Use Hooke's law.

$\Rightarrow 2x = l + 2(2l - x)$ — Divide both sides by mg and multiply through by l.

$\Rightarrow 2x = l + 4l - 2x$

$\Rightarrow 4x = 5l$

$\Rightarrow x = \dfrac{5l}{4}$ — Solve for x.

The distance of the particle below P is $\dfrac{9l}{4}$. — Add on the natural length of the spring.

Exercise 2A

1 One end of a light elastic string is attached to a fixed point. A force of 4 N is applied to the other end of the string so as to stretch it. The natural length of the string is 3 m and the modulus of elasticity is λ N. Find the total length of the string when

   a $\lambda = 30$, **b** $\lambda = 12$, **c** $\lambda = 16$.

2 The length of an elastic spring is reduced to 0.8 m when a force of 20 N compresses it. Given that the modulus of elasticity of the spring is 25 N, find its natural length.

3 An elastic spring of modulus of elasticity 20 N has one end fixed. When a particle of mass 1 kg is attached to the other end and hangs at rest, the total length of the spring is 1.4 m. The particle of mass 1 kg is removed and replaced by a particle of mass 0.8 kg. Find the new length of the spring.

4 A light elastic spring, of natural length a and modulus of elasticity λ, has one end fixed. A scale pan of mass M is attached to its other end and hangs in equilibrium. A mass m is gently placed in the scale pan. Find the distance of the new equilibrium position below the old one.

5 An elastic string has length a_1 when supporting a mass m_1 and length a_2 when supporting a mass m_2. Find the natural length and modulus of elasticity of the string.

6 A light elastic spring has natural length $2a$ and modulus of elasticity $2mg$. A particle of mass m is attached to the mid-point of the spring. One end of the spring, A, is attached to the floor of a room of height $5a$ and the other end is attached to the ceiling of the room at a point B vertically above A. Find the distance of the particle below the ceiling when it is in equilibrium.

7 A uniform rod PQ, of mass $5\,\text{kg}$ and length $3\,\text{m}$, has one end, P, smoothly hinged to a fixed point. The other end, Q, is attached to one end of a light elastic string of modulus of elasticity $30\,\text{N}$. The other end of the string is attached to a fixed point R which is on the same horizontal level as P with $RP = 5\,\text{m}$. The system is in equilibrium and $\angle PQR = 90°$. Find

a the tension in the string,

b the natural length of the string.

8 A light elastic string AB has natural length l and modulus of elasticity $2mg$. Another light elastic string CD has natural length l and modulus of elasticity $4mg$. The strings are joined at their ends B and C and the end A is attached to a fixed point. A particle of mass m is hung from the end D and is at rest in equilibrium. Find the length AD.

9 An elastic string PA has natural length $0.5\,\text{m}$ and modulus of elasticity $9.8\,\text{N}$. The string PB is inextensible. The end A of the elastic string and the end B of the inextensible string are attached to two fixed points which are on the same horizontal level. The end P of each string is attached to a $2\,\text{kg}$ particle. The particle hangs in equilibrium below AB, with PA making an angle of $30°$ with AB and PA perpendicular to PB. Find

a the length of PA,

b the length of PB,

c the tension in PB.

10 A particle of mass $2\,\text{kg}$ is attached to one end P of a light elastic string PQ of modulus of elasticity $20\,\text{N}$ and natural length $0.8\,\text{m}$. The end Q of the string is attached to a point on a rough plane which is inclined at an angle α to the horizontal, where $\tan\alpha = \frac{3}{4}$. The coefficient of friction between the particle and the plane is $\frac{1}{2}$. The particle rests in limiting equilibrium, on the point of sliding down the plane, with PQ along a line of greatest slope. Find

a the tension in the string,

b the length of the string.

2.2 You can use Hooke's law to solve dynamics problems involving elastic strings or springs.

Example 7

One end of a light elastic string, of natural length 0.5 m and modulus of elasticity 20 N, is attached to a fixed point A. The other end of the string is attached to a particle of mass 2 kg. The particle is held at a point which is 1.5 m below A and released from rest. Find.

a the initial acceleration of the particle,

b the length of the string when the particle reaches its maximum speed.

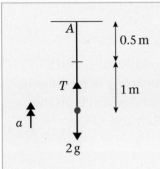

a $(\uparrow)$ $T - 2g = 2a$

    Resolve upwards.

$T = \dfrac{20 \times 1}{0.5}$

    Use Hooke's law.

$= 40\,N$

so, $40 - 19.6 = 2a$

    Substitute for T.

$10.2 = a$

    Solve for a.

The initial acceleration is $10.2\,m\,s^{-2}$

b Particle reaches its maximum speed when it stops accelerating i.e. when its acceleration is zero.

    A very common misconception is that the particle reaches maximum speed just as the elastic goes slack.

$T - 2g = 0$

$T = 2g$

    Maximum speed occurs at the equilibrium position.

$\dfrac{20x}{0.5} = 2g$

$x = \dfrac{g}{20}$

$= 0.49$

So the length of the string is

$0.5 + 0.49 = 0.99\,m$

    Add on the natural length to the extension.

Draw a diagram showing all the forces and the acceleration of the particle. Note that, although the particle is (instantaneously) at rest, it has an upward acceleration.

Example 8

A particle of mass 0.5 kg is attached to one end of a light elastic spring of natural length 1.5 m and modulus of elasticity 19.6 N. The other end of the spring is attached to a fixed point O on a rough plane which is inclined to the horizontal at an angle α, where $\tan \alpha = \frac{3}{4}$. The coefficient of friction between the particle and the plane is 0.2. The particle is held at rest on the plane at a point which is 1 m from O down a line of greatest slope of the plane. The particle is released from rest and moves down the slope. Find its initial acceleration.

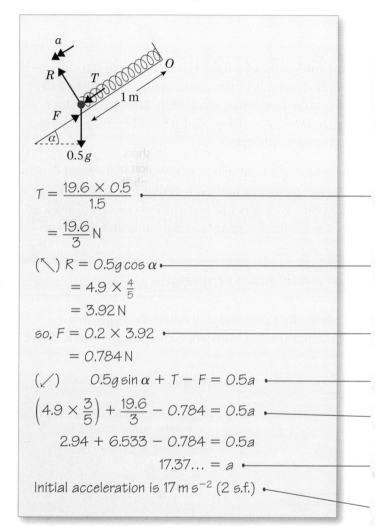

Draw a diagram showing all four forces acting on the particle and the acceleration. Note that, since the spring is compressed, it will be in compression, i.e. T acts **down** the plane.

$$T = \frac{19.6 \times 0.5}{1.5}$$

By Hooke's law.

$$= \frac{19.6}{3} \text{ N}$$

$$(\nwarrow) \quad R = 0.5g \cos \alpha$$

There is no acceleration perpendicular to the plane.

$$= 4.9 \times \frac{4}{5}$$

$$= 3.92 \text{ N}$$

so, $F = 0.2 \times 3.92$

$F = \mu R$ since the particle is about to move.

$$= 0.784 \text{ N}$$

$$(\swarrow) \quad 0.5g \sin \alpha + T - F = 0.5a$$

Resolve down the plane.

$$\left(4.9 \times \frac{3}{5}\right) + \frac{19.6}{3} - 0.784 = 0.5a$$

Substitute for T and F.

$$2.94 + 6.533 - 0.784 = 0.5a$$

$$17.37\ldots = a$$

Solve for a.

Initial acceleration is 17 m s^{-2} (2 s.f.)

Round answer to 2 s.f. since $g = 9.8$ has been used.

Exercise 2B

1 A particle of mass 4 kg is attached to one end P of a light elastic spring PQ, of natural length 0.5 m and modulus of elasticity 40 N. The spring rests on a smooth horizontal plane with the end Q fixed. the particle is held at rest and then released. Find the initial acceleration of the particle

a if $PQ = 0.8$ m initially,

b if $PQ = 0.4$ m initially.

2 A particle of mass 0.4 kg is fixed to one end A of a light elastic spring AB, of natural length 0.8 m and modulus of elasticity 20 N. The other end B of the spring is attached to a fixed point. The particle hangs in equilibrium. It is then pulled vertically downwards through a distance 0.2 m and released from rest. Find the initial acceleration of the particle.

3

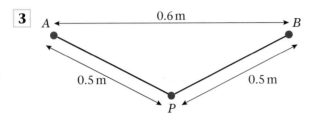

A particle P of mass 2 kg is attached to the mid-point of a light elastic string, of natural length 0.4 m and modulus of elasticity 20 N. The ends of the elastic string are attached to two fixed points A and B which are on the same horizontal level, with $AB = 0.6$ m. The particle is held in the position shown, with $AP = BP = 0.5$ m, and released from rest. Find the initial acceleration of the particle and state its direction.

4 A particle of mass 2 kg is attached to one end P of a light elastic spring. The other end Q of the spring is attached to a fixed point O. The spring has natural length 1.5 m and modulus of elasticity 40 N. The particle is held at a point which is 1 m vertically above O and released from rest. Find the initial acceleration of the particle, stating its magnitude and direction.

2.3 You can find the energy stored in an elastic string or spring.

You can draw a **force–distance** diagram to show the extension x in an elastic string as a gradually increasing force is applied. The area under the force–distance graph is the **work done** in stretching the elastic string.

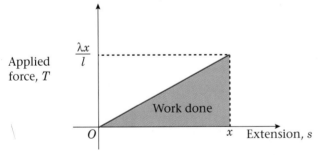

λ is the modulus of elasticity of the string and l is its natural length.

The applied force is always equal and opposite to the tension in the elastic string, T. This value increases as the string stretches.

Using the formula for the area of a triangle:

$$\text{Area} = \frac{1}{2}x\left(\frac{\lambda x}{l}\right)$$

$$= \frac{\lambda x^2}{2l}$$

Using integration:

$$\text{Area} = \int_0^x T\, ds$$

$$= \int_0^x \frac{\lambda s}{l}\, ds$$

$$= \left[\frac{\lambda s^2}{2l}\right]_0^x$$

$$= \frac{\lambda x^2}{2l}$$

- The work done in stretching an elastic string or spring of modulus of elasticity λ from its natural length l to a length $(l + x)$ is $\frac{\lambda x^2}{2l}$.

When λ is measured in newtons and x and l are measured in metres, the work done is in **Joules (J)**.

When a stretched string is released it will 'ping' back to its natural length. In its stretched position it has the potential to do work, or **elastic potential energy**.

- The elastic potential energy (E.P.E.) stored in a stretched string or spring is exactly equal to the amount of work done to stretch the string or spring.

- The E.P.E. stored in an elastic string or spring of modulus of elasticity λ which has been stretched from its natural length l to a length $(l + x)$ is $\frac{\lambda x^2}{2l}$.

You can apply the same formulae for work done and elastic potential energy when an elastic string or spring is compressed.

Example 9

An elastic string has natural length 1.4 m and modulus of elasticity 6 N. Find the energy stored in the string when its length is 1.6 m.

Energy stored $= \frac{6 \times 0.2^2}{2 \times 1.4}$

Use $\frac{\lambda x^2}{2l}$ when $x = 1.6 - 1.4 = 0.2$.

$= 0.0857 \, \text{J} \ (3 \text{ s.f.})$

Example 10

A light elastic spring has natural length 0.6 m and modulus of elasticity 10 N. Find the work done in compressing the spring from a length of 0.5 m to a length of 0.3 m.

$$\text{Work done in compression} = \text{Energy stored when length is 0.3 m} - \text{Energy stored when length is 0.5 m}$$

$$= \frac{10 \times 0.3^2}{2 \times 0.6} - \frac{10 \times 0.1^2}{2 \times 0.6}$$

$$= \frac{10}{1.2}(0.3^2 - 0.1^2)$$

$$= \frac{25}{3}(0.3 + 0.1)(0.3 - 0.1)$$

$$= \frac{25}{3} \times 0.4 \times 0.2$$

$$= \frac{2}{3} \, \text{J}$$

A common error is to use:

$\frac{10 \times (0.3 - 0.1)^2}{2 \times 0.6}$

which is not the same.

Exercise 2C

1 An elastic spring has natural length 0.6 m and modulus of elasticity 8 N. Find the work done when the spring is stretched from its natural length to a length of 1 m.

2 An elastic spring, of natural length 0.8 m and modulus of elasticity of 4 N, is compressed to a length of 0.6 m. Find the elastic potential energy stored in the spring.

3 An elastic string has natural length 1.2 m and modulus of elasticity 10 N. Find the work done when the string is stretched from a length 1.5 m to a length 1.8 m.

4 An elastic spring has natural length 0.7 m and modulus of elasticity 20 N. Find the work done when the spring is stretched from a length

    a 0.7 m to 0.9 m

    b 0.8 m to 1.0 m

    c 1.2 m to 1.4 m.

> Note that your answer to **a**, **b** and **c** are all different.

5 A light elastic spring has natural length 1.2 m and modulus of elasticity 10 N. One end of the spring is attached to a fixed point. A particle of mass 2 kg is attached to the other end and hangs in equilibrium. Find the energy stored in the spring.

6 An elastic string has natural length a. One end is fixed. A particle of mass $2m$ is attached to the free end and hangs in equilibrium, with the length of the string $3a$. Find the elastic potential energy stored in the string.

2.4 You can solve problems involving elastic energy using the conservation of energy principle and the work–energy principle.

In M2 the conservation of energy principle was applied to problems involving kinetic and potential energy. You can use this principle to solve problems involving elastic energy.

If a particle which is attached to an elastic spring or string is subject to a resistance as it moves you will need to apply the work–energy principle.

Example 11

A light elastic string, of natural length 1.6 m and modulus of elasticity 10 N, has one end fixed at a point A on a smooth horizontal table. A particle of mass 2 kg is attached to the other end of the string. The particle is held at the point A and projected horizontally along the table with speed $2 \, \text{m s}^{-1}$. Find how far it travels before first coming to instantaneous rest.

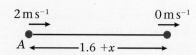

Suppose that the extension of the string when the particle comes to rest is x.

K.E. lost by the particle = E.P.E. gained by the string

$$\left(\tfrac{1}{2}mv^2\right) = \left(\frac{\lambda x^2}{2l}\right)$$

$$\tfrac{1}{2} \times 2 \times 2^2 = \frac{10x^2}{2 \times 1.6}$$

$$1.28 = x^2$$

$$1.13 = x$$

∴ Total distance travelled is 2.73 m

Draw a simple diagram showing the initial and final positions of the particle.

You can apply the conservation of energy principle since the table is smooth i.e. no friction.

Note that you do not need to consider an intermediate position.

Add on the natural length of the string.

It is important to realise that the particle is not in equilibrium when it comes to instantaneous rest and so we cannot use forces to solve this type of problem. The particle in fact has an acceleration and will 'spring' back towards A.

Example 12

A particle of mass 0.5 kg is attached to one end of an elastic string, of natural length 2 m and modulus of elasticity 19.6 N. The other end of the elastic string is attached to the point O. If the particle is released from the point O, find the greatest distance it will reach below O.

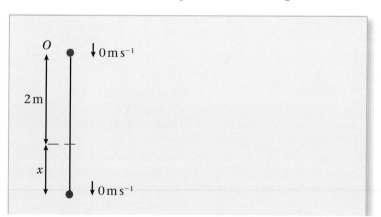

Draw a diagram showing the initial and final positions of the particle. Let the extension of the string be x when the particle comes to rest.

P.E. loss of particle = E.P.E. gained by string

$$(mgh) = \left(\frac{\lambda x^2}{2l}\right)$$

$$0.5g(2 + x) = \frac{19.6x^2}{4}$$

$$2 + x = x^2$$

$$0 = x^2 - x - 2$$

$$0 = (x - 2)(x + 1)$$

$$x = 2 \text{ or } -1$$

Hence particle falls a distance of 4 m before coming to rest.

> There is no K.E. involved as the particle starts at rest and finishes at rest. Assuming no air resistance, energy will be conserved.

> Simplify.

> Collect terms.

> Factorise.

> We can ignore the negative solution.

Example 13

A light elastic spring, of natural length 1 m and modulus of elasticity 10 N, has one end attached to a fixed point A. A particle of mass 2 kg is attached to the other end of the spring and is held at a point B which is 0.8 m vertically below A. The particle is projected vertically downwards from B with speed 2 m s^{-1}. Find the distance it falls before first coming to rest.

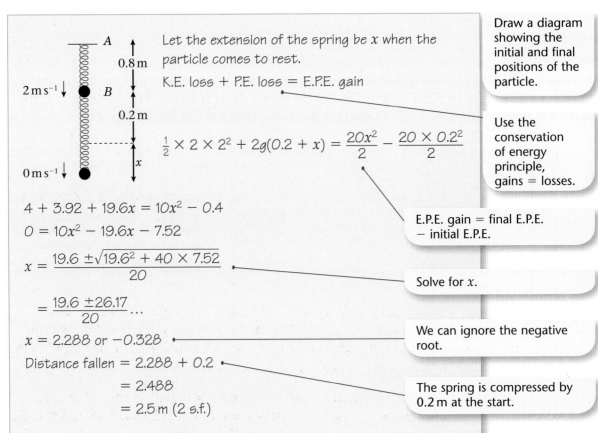

Let the extension of the spring be x when the particle comes to rest.

K.E. loss + P.E. loss = E.P.E. gain

$$\frac{1}{2} \times 2 \times 2^2 + 2g(0.2 + x) = \frac{20x^2}{2} - \frac{20 \times 0.2^2}{2}$$

$$4 + 3.92 + 19.6x = 10x^2 - 0.4$$

$$0 = 10x^2 - 19.6x - 7.52$$

$$x = \frac{19.6 \pm \sqrt{19.6^2 + 40 \times 7.52}}{20}$$

$$= \frac{19.6 \pm 26.17}{20}\ldots$$

$$x = 2.288 \text{ or } -0.328$$

Distance fallen = 2.288 + 0.2

$$= 2.488$$

$$= 2.5 \text{ m (2 s.f.)}$$

> Draw a diagram showing the initial and final positions of the particle.

> Use the conservation of energy principle, gains = losses.

> E.P.E. gain = final E.P.E. − initial E.P.E.

> Solve for x.

> We can ignore the negative root.

> The spring is compressed by 0.2 m at the start.

Example 14

A light elastic spring, of natural length 0.5 m and modulus of elasticity 10 N, has one end attached to a point A on a rough horizontal plane. The other end is attached to a particle P of mass 0.8 kg. The coefficient of friction between the particle and the plane is 0.4. The particle initially lies on the plane with $AP = 0.5$ m and is then projected with speed $2\,\mathrm{m\,s^{-1}}$ away from A along the plane. Find the distance moved by P before it first comes to rest.

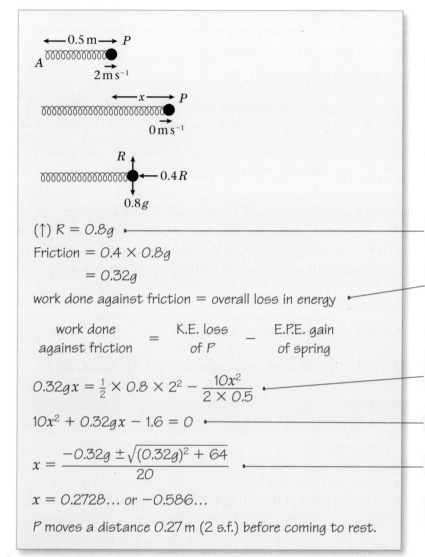

Draw a diagram showing the initial and final positions of the particle.

As it slides, P will be moving against friction, μR, from the plane.

$(\uparrow)\ R = 0.8g$ — First find the magnitude of the friction force.

Friction $= 0.4 \times 0.8g$

$\qquad = 0.32g$

work done against friction $=$ overall loss in energy — Apply the work–energy principle.

$$\begin{array}{c} \text{work done} \\ \text{against friction} \end{array} = \begin{array}{c} \text{K.E. loss} \\ \text{of } P \end{array} - \begin{array}{c} \text{E.P.E. gain} \\ \text{of spring} \end{array}$$

losses $-$ gains

$$0.32gx = \tfrac{1}{2} \times 0.8 \times 2^2 - \frac{10x^2}{2 \times 0.5}$$

Use force $\times$ distance, $\tfrac{1}{2}mv^2$ and $\dfrac{\lambda x^2}{2l}$.

$10x^2 + 0.32gx - 1.6 = 0$ — Collect terms.

$$x = \frac{-0.32g \pm \sqrt{(0.32g)^2 + 64}}{20}$$

Solve for x.

$x = 0.2728\ldots$ or $-0.586\ldots$

We can ignore the negative root.

P moves a distance 0.27 m (2 s.f.) before coming to rest.

Exercise 2D

1. An elastic string, of natural length l and modulus of elasticity mg, has one end fixed to a point A on a smooth horizontal table. The other end is attached to a particle P of mass m. The particle is held at a point on the table with $AP = \frac{3}{2}l$ and is released. Find the speed of the particle when the string reaches its natural length.

2. A particle of mass m is suspended from a fixed point O by a light elastic string, of natural length a and modulus of elasticity $4mg$. The particle is pulled vertically downwards a distance d from its equilibrium position and released from rest. If the particle just reaches O, find d.

3 A light elastic spring of natural length $2l$ has its ends attached to two points P and Q which are at the same horizontal level. The length PQ is $2l$. A particle of mass m is fastened to the mid-point of the spring and is held at the mid-point of PQ. The particle is released from rest and first comes to instantaneous rest when both parts of the string make an angle of $60°$ with the line PQ. Find the modulus of elasticity of the spring.

4 A light elastic string, of natural length 1 m and modulus of elasticity 21.6 N has one end attached to a fixed point O. A particle of mass 2 kg is attached to the other end. The particle is held at a point which is 3 m vertically below O and released from rest. Find

  a the speed of the particle when the string first becomes slack,

  b the distance from O when the particle first comes to rest.

5 A particle P is attached to one end of a light elastic string of natural length a. The other end of the string is attached to a fixed point O. When P hangs at rest in equilibrium, the distance OP is $\frac{5a}{3}$. The particle is now projected vertically downwards from O with speed U and first comes to instantaneous rest at a distance $\frac{10a}{3}$ below O. Find U in terms of a and g.

6 A particle P of mass 1 kg is attached to the mid-point of a light elastic string, of natural length 3 m and modulus λ N. The ends of the string are attached to two points A and B on the same horizontal level with $AB = 3$ m. The particle is held at the mid-point of AB and released from rest. The particle falls vertically and comes to instantaneous rest at a point which is 1 m below the mid-point of AB. Find

  a the value of λ,

  b the speed of P when it is 0.5 m below the initial position.

7 A light elastic string of natural length 2 m and modulus of elasticity 117.6 N has one end attached to a fixed point O. A particle P of mass 3 kg is attached to the other end. The particle is held at O and released from rest.

  a Find the distance fallen by P before it first comes to rest.

  b Find the greatest speed of P during the fall.

8 A particle P of mass 2 kg is attached to one end of a light elastic string of natural length 1 m and modulus of elasticity 40 N. The other end of the string is fixed to a point O on a rough plane which is inclined at an angle α, where $\tan \alpha = \frac{3}{4}$. The particle is held at O and released from rest. Given that P comes to rest after moving 2 m down the plane, find the coefficient of friction between the particle and the plane.

Mixed exercise 2E

1 A particle of mass m is supported by two light elastic strings, each of natural length a and modulus of elasticity $\frac{15mg}{16}$. The other ends of the strings are attached to two fixed points A and B where A and B are in the same horizontal line with $AB = 2a$. When the particle hangs at rest in equilibrium below AB, each string makes an angle θ with the vertical.

  a Verify that $\cos \theta = \frac{4}{5}$.

  b How much work must be down to raise the particle to the mid-point of AB?

2 A light elastic spring is such that a weight of magnitude W resting on the spring produces a compression a. The weight W is allowed to fall onto the spring from a height of $\frac{3a}{2}$ above it. Find the maximum compression of the spring in the subsequent motion.

3 A light elastic string of natural length $0.5\,\text{m}$ is stretched between two points P and Q on a smooth horizontal table. The distance PQ is $0.75\,\text{m}$ and the tension in the string is $15\,\text{N}$.

  a Find the modulus of elasticity of the string.

A particle of mass $0.5\,\text{kg}$ is attached to the mid-point of the string. The particle is pulled $0.1\,\text{m}$ towards Q and released from rest.

  b Find the speed of the particle as it passes through the mid-point of PQ.

4 A particle P of mass m is attached to two strings AP and BP. The points A and B are on the same horizontal level and $AB = \frac{5a}{4}$.

The string AP is inextensible and $AP = \frac{3a}{4}$.

The string BP is elastic and $BP = a$.

The modulus of elasticity of BP is λ. Show that the natural length of BP is $\dfrac{5\lambda a}{3mg + 5\lambda}$.

5 A light elastic string, of natural length a and modulus of elasticity $5mg$, has one end attached to the base of a vertical wall. The other end of the string is attached to a small ball. The ball is held at a distance $\frac{3a}{2}$ from the wall, on a rough horizontal plane, and released from rest. The coefficient of friction between the ball and the plane is $\frac{1}{5}$.

  a Find, in terms of a and g, the speed V of the ball as it hits the wall.

The ball rebounds from the wall with speed $\frac{2V}{5}$.

  b Find the distance from the wall at which the ball comes to rest.

6 **a** Using integration, show that the work done in stretching a light elastic string of natural length l and modulus of elasticity λ, from length l to length $(l + x)$ is $\dfrac{\lambda x^2}{2l}$.

  b The same string is stretched from a length $(l + a)$ to a length $(l + b)$ where $b > a$.

Show that the work done is the product of the mean tension and the distance moved.

7 A light elastic string has natural length l and modulus $2mg$. One end of the string is attached to a particle P of mass m. The other end is attached to a fixed point C on a rough horizontal plane. Initially P is at rest at a point D on the plane where $CD = \frac{4l}{3}$.

  a Given that P is in limiting equilibrium, find the coefficient of friction between P and the plane.

The particle P is now moved away from C to a point E on the plane where $CE = 2l$.

  b Find the speed of P when the string returns to its natural length.

  c Find the total distance moved by P before it comes to rest.

8 A light elastic string of natural length 0.2 m has its ends attached to two fixed points A and B which are on the same horizontal level with $AB = 0.2$ m. A particle of mass 5 kg is attached to the string at the point P where $AP = 0.15$ m. The system is released and P hangs in equilibrium below AB with $A\hat{P}B = 90°$.

   a If $B\hat{A}P = \theta$, show that the ratio of the extension of AP and BP is

$$\frac{4\cos\theta - 3}{4\sin\theta - 1}.$$

   b Hence show that

$$\cos\theta\,(4\cos\theta - 3) = 3\sin\theta\,(4\sin\theta - 1).$$

9 A particle of mass 3 kg is attached to one end of a light elastic string, of natural length 1 m and modulus of elasticity 14.7 N. The other end of the string is attached to a fixed point. The particle is held in equilibrium by a horizontal force of magnitude 9.8 N with the string inclined to the vertical at an angle θ.

   a Find the value of θ.

   b Find the extension of the string.

   c If the horizontal force is removed, find the magnitude of the least force that will keep the string inclined at the same angle.

10 Two points A and B are on the same horizontal level with $AB = 3a$. A particle P of mass m is joined to A by a light inextensible string of length $4a$ and is joined to B by a light elastic string, of natural length a and modulus of elasticity $\dfrac{mg}{4}$. The particle P is held at the point C, on AB produced, such that $BC = a$ and both strings are taut. The particle P is released from rest.

   a Show that when AP is vertical the speed of P is $2\sqrt{ga}$.

   b Find the tension in the elastic string in this position.

Summary of key points

1 Elastic strings and springs have a tension or thrust, T, given by

$$T = \frac{\lambda x}{l}$$

This is called Hooke's law.

   where λ is the modulus of elasticity, l is the natural (unstretched) length of the string or spring and x is the extension or compression.

2 The work done in stretching (or compressing) an elastic string (or spring) with modulus of elasticity λ and natural length l from its natural length to a length $(l + x)$ is $\dfrac{\lambda x^2}{2l}$.

3 The elastic potential energy (E.P.E.) stored in a string or spring of modulus of elasticity λ which is stretched (or compressed) by a length x from its natural length, l, is $\dfrac{\lambda x^2}{2l}$.

4 The work done on a system by external forces (excluding weights) is equal to the total change in the mechanical energy of the system (i.e. the K.E., P.E. and E.P.E.). This is the work–energy principle.

After completing this chapter you should be able to:

- solve problems involving the motion of a particle in a straight line when the force is expressed as a function of either time or distance

- solve problems about a particle moving away from or towards the Earth under the action of the Earth's gravitational force

- model an object oscillating about a fixed point with simple harmonic motion (S.H.M.)

- investigate the motion of a particle which is attached to the end of an elastic string or spring and is set in motion.

Further dynamics

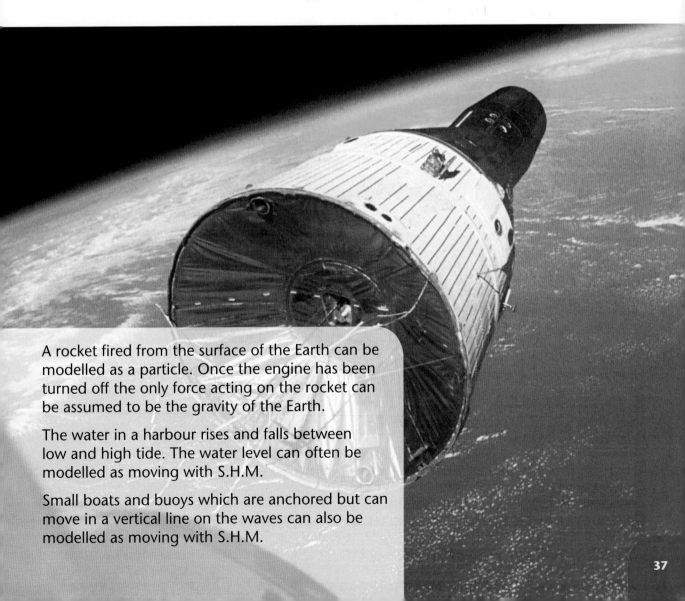

A rocket fired from the surface of the Earth can be modelled as a particle. Once the engine has been turned off the only force acting on the rocket can be assumed to be the gravity of the Earth.

The water in a harbour rises and falls between low and high tide. The water level can often be modelled as moving with S.H.M.

Small boats and buoys which are anchored but can move in a vertical line on the waves can also be modelled as moving with S.H.M.

3.1 **3.1** **You can use calculus to apply Newton's laws to a particle moving in a straight line when the applied force is variable.**

Consider a particle of mass m moving in a straight line under the action of a force F which is a function of time:

$F = F(t)$

$ma = F(t)$

> Use Newton's second law, $F = ma$.

As the force is variable, the acceleration will also be variable, so replace a with $\dfrac{dv}{dt}$.

■ $m\dfrac{dv}{dt} = F(t)$

> Integrate with respect to time.

$mv = \int F(t)\, dt + C$

where c is the constant of integration.

> Most mechanics questions will include information to enable you to calculate the value of C.

Sometimes the force F is given as a function of the displacement:

$F = G(x)$

$ma = G(x)$

> Use Newton's second law, $F = ma$.

As the integration must be with respect to x, use $a = \dfrac{d}{dx}\left(\tfrac{1}{2}v^2\right) = v\dfrac{dv}{dx}$.

■ $mv\dfrac{dv}{dx} = G(x)$

$\tfrac{1}{2}mv^2 = \int G(x)\, dx + K$

> Integrate with respect to x.

■ **When the applied force is a function of time, use**

$a = \dfrac{dv}{dt}$

■ **When the applied force is a function of displacement, use**

$a = \dfrac{d}{dx}\left(\tfrac{1}{2}v^2\right) = v\dfrac{dv}{dx}$

> See book M1, Chapter 3.

Impulse and momentum

The impulse momentum equation $\mathbf{F}t = m\mathbf{v} - m\mathbf{u}$ is used when the applied force is constant. When the applied force is a function of time, you use

$F(t) = m\dfrac{dv}{dt}$

In the time interval t_1 to t_2 the particle's velocity changes from U to V and, by using definite integration,

$$\int_{t_1}^{t_2} F(t)\,dt = m\int_U^V 1\,dv$$

$$= m[v]_U^V$$

$$= m(V - U)$$

$$= mV - mU$$

> This is the change of momentum of the particle.

The quantity $\int_{t_1}^{t_2} F(t)\,dt$ is the **impulse** of the variable force on the particle.

■ **For a variable force,**

- **impulse = change of momentum**

- **impulse** $= \int_{t_1}^{t_2} \mathbf{F}(t)\,d\mathbf{t}$

Work and energy

When a constant force acts on a particle and moves it through a distance s in the direction of the force, the work done by the force is defined by:

$$\text{Work done} = F \times s$$

> See book M2, Chapter 3.

Also, $\qquad Fs = \frac{1}{2}mv^2 - \frac{1}{2}mu^2$

where u and v are the initial and final speeds of the particle.

When the applied force is a function of displacement, you use

$$G(x) = mv\frac{dv}{dx}$$

If the particle increases its speed from U to V while moving from the point where $x = x_1$ to the point where $x = x_2$, then using definite integration with respect to x gives

$$\int_{x_2}^{x_1} G(x)\,dx = m\int_U^V v\,dv$$

> $\int_{x_1}^{x_2} G(x)\,dx$ is the work done by the variable force.

$$= m\left[\tfrac{1}{2}v^2\right]_U^V$$

$$= \tfrac{1}{2}mV^2 - \tfrac{1}{2}mU^2$$

> This is the increase in kinetic energy of the particle.

■ **For a variable force,**

- **work done by the force = increase in kinetic energy**

- **work done** $= \int_{x_1}^{x_2} \mathbf{G}(\mathbf{x})\,d\mathbf{x}$

Example 1

A particle P of mass 0.5 kg is moving along the x-axis. At time t seconds the force acting on P has magnitude $(5t^2 + e^{0.2t})$ N and acts in the direction OP. When $t = 0$, P is at rest at O. Calculate

a the speed of P when $t = 2$,

b the distance OP when $t = 3$.

a $F = ma$

$5t^2 + e^{0.2t} = 0.5a$

> Use $F = ma$ with $F = 5t^2 + e^{0.2t}$ and $m = 0.5$.

$0.5\dfrac{dv}{dt} = 5t^2 + e^{0.2t}$

> Replace a with $\dfrac{dv}{dt}$.

$0.5v = \dfrac{5}{3}t^3 + \dfrac{1}{0.2}e^{0.2t} + C$

> Integrate with respect to t.

$v = \dfrac{10}{3}t^3 + 10e^{0.2t} + D$

> Divide by 0.5. Change C to D instead of dividing.

$t = 0, v = 0 \Rightarrow 0 = 0 + 10 + D$

$\therefore D = -10$ and $v = \dfrac{10}{3}t^3 + 10e^{0.2t} - 10$

> Use $v = 0$ when $t = 0$ to find the value of D and complete the expression for v.

$t = 2, v = \dfrac{80}{3} + 10e^{0.4} - 10 = 30.58...$

When $t = 2$ the speed of P is $30.6\,\mathrm{m\,s^{-1}}$ (3 s.f.).

> Now substitute $t = 2$ to obtain the required value.

b $v = \dfrac{10}{3}t^3 + 10e^{0.2t} - 10$

$\dfrac{dx}{dt} = \dfrac{10}{3}t^3 + 10e^{0.2t} - 10$

> Replace v with $\dfrac{dx}{dt}$.

$x = \dfrac{10}{12}t^4 + \dfrac{10}{0.2}e^{0.2t} - 10t + K$

> Integrate with respect to t. Use a different letter for the constant of integration.

$t = 0, x = 0 \Rightarrow 0 = 0 + 50 - 0 + K$

$\therefore K = -50$ and $x = \dfrac{10}{12}t^4 + \dfrac{10}{0.2}e^{0.2t} - 10t - 50$

> Use the initial conditions to find K.

$t = 3 \Rightarrow x = \dfrac{10}{12} \times 3^4 + \dfrac{10}{0.2}e^{0.6} - 10 \times 3 - 50 = 14.94...$

When $t = 3$, OP is $14.9\,\mathrm{m}$ (3 s.f.).

> Now substitute $t = 3$ to obtain the required value.

Example 2

A particle P of mass 1.5 kg is moving in a straight line. The force acting on P has magnitude $(8 - 2\cos x)$ N, where x metres is the distance OP, and acts in the direction OP. When P passes through O its speed is $4\,\text{m s}^{-1}$. Calculate the speed of P when $x = 2$.

$F = ma$

$8 - 2\cos x = 1.5a$

$1.5v\dfrac{dv}{dx} = 8 - 2\cos x$

$1.5\displaystyle\int v\,dv = \int(8 - 2\cos x)\,dx$

$1.5 \times \tfrac{1}{2}v^2 = 8x - 2\sin x + C$

$x = 0, v = 4 \Rightarrow 1.5 \times \tfrac{1}{2} \times 4^2 = 0 - 0 + C$

$\therefore C = 12$ and $0.75v^2 = 8x - 2\sin x + 12$

$x = 2 \Rightarrow 0.75v^2 = 8 \times 2 - 2\sin 2 + 12$

$v = 5.908...$

When $x = 2$ the speed of P is $5.91\,\text{m s}^{-1}$ (3 s.f.).

Use $F = ma$ with $F = 8 - 2\cos x$ and $m = 1.5$.

As F is a function of x, replace a with $v\dfrac{dv}{dx}$.

Separate the variables and integrate with respect to x.

Use the initial conditions to find C.

Substitute $x = 2$ to find the required speed.
Remember that as calculus has been used, x must be in radians.

Example 3

A pebble of mass 0.2 kg is moving on a smooth horizontal sheet of ice. At time t seconds (where $t \geqslant 0$) a horizontal force of magnitude $2t^2$ N and constant direction acts on the pebble. When $t = 0$ the pebble is moving in the same direction as the force and has speed $6\,\text{m s}^{-1}$. When $t = T$ the pebble has speed $36\,\text{m s}^{-1}$. Calculate the value of T.

Method 1: Using the impulse-momentum equation:

$\displaystyle\int_{t_1}^{t_2} F(t)\,dt = mV - mU$

$\displaystyle\int_0^T (2t^2)\,dt = 0.2 \times 36 - 0.2 \times 6$

$\left[\dfrac{2}{3}t^3\right]_0^T = 6$

$T^3 = \dfrac{3}{2} \times 6$

$T = 2.080...$

$T = 2.08$ (3 s.f.)

Use $\displaystyle\int_{t_1}^{t_2} F(t)\,dt = mV - mU$ with $F = 2t^2$, $t_1 = 0$, $t_2 = T$, $m = 0.2$, $V = 36$ and $U = 6$.

Integrate with respect to t.

Substitute the limits and solve for T.

Method 2: Using Newton's second law:

$F = ma$

$0.2\dfrac{dv}{dt} = 2t^2$ •————————

$0.2v = \dfrac{2}{3}t^3 + C$

$t = 0, v = 6 \Rightarrow 0.2 \times 6 = 0 + C$ •

$\therefore C = 1.2$ and $0.2v = \dfrac{2}{3}t^3 + 1.2$

$t = T, v = 36 \Rightarrow 0.2 \times 36 + \dfrac{2}{3}T^3 + 1.2$ •

$T^3 = \dfrac{3}{2} \times 6$

$T = 2.080\ldots$

$T = 2.08$ (3 s.f.)

> Use $F = ma$ with $F = 2t^2$ and $m = 0.2$.
> As F is a function of t replace a with $\dfrac{dv}{dt}$.

> Integrate with respect to t and use the initial conditions to find the value of C.

> Substitute $t = T$ and solve for T.

Example 4

A stone S of mass $0.5\,\text{kg}$ is moving in a straight line on a smooth horizontal floor. When S is a distance x metres from a fixed point on the line, A, a force of magnitude $(5 + 7\cos x)\,\text{N}$ acts on S in the direction AS. Given that S passes through A with speed $2\,\text{m s}^{-1}$, calculate

i the work done by the force in moving S from A to the point B, where $x = 3$,

ii the speed of S as it passes through B.

Method 1: Using work and energy:

i Work done $= \displaystyle\int_{x_1}^{x_2} F(x)\,dx$ •

Work done $= \displaystyle\int_{0}^{3} (5 + 7\cos x)\,dx$

$\qquad = [5x + 7\sin x]_0^3$

$\qquad = (15 + 7\sin 3) - 0$ •

$\qquad = 15.98\ldots$

The work done is $16.0\,\text{J}$ (3 s.f.).

> Use work done $= \displaystyle\int_{x_1}^{x_2} F\,dx$ with $F = 5 + 7\cos x$, $x_1 = 0$ and $x_2 = 3$.

> Remember to have your calculator in radian mode.

ii Work done $=$ increase in K.E. $= \dfrac{1}{2}mv^2 - \dfrac{1}{2}mu^2$

$15.98 = \dfrac{1}{2} \times 0.5v^2 - \dfrac{1}{2} \times 0.5 \times 2^2$ •

$0.25v^2 = 15.98 + 1$

$v = 8.241\ldots$ •

S passes through B with speed $8.24\,\text{m s}^{-1}$ (3 s.f.).

> Use work done $= \dfrac{1}{2}mv^2 - \dfrac{1}{2}mu^2$ with work $= 15.98$, $m = 0.5$ and $u = 2$.

> Solve for v. You can ignore the negative root.

Method 2: Using Newton's second law:

$F = ma$

$0.5v\dfrac{dv}{dx} = 5 + 7\cos x$

$\displaystyle\int 0.5v\,dv = \int(5 + 7\cos x)\,dx$

$0.5 \times \tfrac{1}{2}v^2 = 5x + 7\sin x + C$

$x = 0, v = 2 \Rightarrow 0.5 \times \tfrac{1}{2} \times 2^2 = C$

$\therefore C = 1$ and $\tfrac{1}{4}v^2 = 5x + 7\sin x + 1$

$x = 3 \Rightarrow v^2 = 4(15 + 7\sin 3 + 1)$

$v^2 = 67.95\ldots$

$v = 8.243\ldots$

ii S passes through B with speed $8.24\,\text{m s}^{-1}$ (3 s.f.)

Work done = increase in K.E.

$= \tfrac{1}{2} \times 0.5 \times 67.95 - \tfrac{1}{2} \times 0.5 \times 2^2$

$= 15.98\ldots$

i The work done is $16.0\,\text{J}$ (3 s.f.).

> This method gives the answer for **ii** before the answer for **i**. This is acceptable in the examination as long as the whole solution is in a logical order and the answers for the two parts are clearly identified.

> Use $F = ma$ with $F = 5 + 7\cos x$ and $m = 0.5$.
> As F is a function of x, replace a with $v\dfrac{dv}{dx}$.

> Separate the variables and integrate. Use the initial conditions to find the value of C.

> Substitute $x = 3$ to find the value of v.

> The work done is now found by considering the increase in K.E. Remember to use an unrounded value of v in your calculation.

Exercise 3A

1 A particle P of mass $0.2\,\text{kg}$ is moving on the x-axis. At time t seconds P is x metres from the origin O. The force acting on P has magnitude $2\cos t\,\text{N}$ and acts in the direction OP. When $t = 0$, P is at rest at O. Calculate

  a the speed of P when $t = 2$,

  b the speed of P when $t = 3$,

  c the time when P first comes to instantaneous rest,

  d the distance OP when $t = 2$,

  e the distance OP when P first comes to instantaneous rest.

2 A van of mass $1200\,\text{kg}$ moves along a horizontal straight road. At time t seconds, the resultant force acting on the car has magnitude $\dfrac{60\,000}{(t + 5)^2}\,\text{N}$ and acts in the direction of motion of the van. When $t = 0$, the van is at rest. The speed of the van approaches a limiting value $V\,\text{m s}^{-1}$. Find

  a the value of V,

  b the distance moved by the van in the first 4 seconds of its motion.

3 A particle P of mass $0.8\,\text{kg}$ is moving along the x-axis. At time $t = 0$, P passes through the origin O, moving in the positive x direction. At time t seconds, $OP = x$ metres and the velocity of P is $v\,\text{m\,s}^{-1}$. The resultant force acting on P has magnitude $\frac{1}{6}(15 - x)\,\text{N}$, and acts in the positive x direction. The maximum speed of P is $12\,\text{m\,s}^{-1}$.

a Explain why the maximum speed of P occurs when $x = 15$.

b Find the speed of P when $t = 0$.

4 A particle P of mass $0.75\,\text{kg}$ is moving in a straight line. At time t seconds after it passes through a fixed point on the line, O, the distance OP is x metres and the force acting on P has magnitude $(2e^{-x} + 2)\,\text{N}$ and acts in the direction OP. Given that P passes through O with speed $5\,\text{m\,s}^{-1}$, calculate the speed of P when

a $x = 3$,

b $x = 7$.

5 A particle P of mass $0.5\,\text{kg}$ moves away from the origin O along the positive x-axis.

When $OP = x$ metres the force acting on P has magnitude $\dfrac{3}{x + 2}\,\text{N}$ and is directed away from O. When $x = 0$ the speed of P is $1.5\,\text{m\,s}^{-1}$. Find the value of x when the speed of P is $2\,\text{m\,s}^{-1}$.

6 Calculate the magnitude of the impulse of a force of magnitude $F\,\text{N}$ acting from time t_1 seconds to time t_2 seconds where

a $F = 3t^2 - \frac{1}{2}t$ $t_1 = 0, t_2 = 4$,

b $F = 2t + \dfrac{1}{3t - 2}$ $t_1 = 1, t_2 = 2$,

c $F = 2\cos 4t$ $t_1 = 0, t_2 = \dfrac{\pi}{4}$,

d $F = 3 + e^{-0.5t}$ $t_1 = 0, t_2 = 4$.

7 Calculate the work done by a force of magnitude $F\,\text{N}$ directed along the x-axis which moves a particle from $x = x_1$ metres to $x = x_2$ metres where

a $F = 2x^{\frac{1}{2}} + \frac{1}{2}x^2$ $x_1 = 1, x_2 = 4$,

b $F = 2\sin x + 3$ $x_1 = 0, x_2 = \dfrac{\pi}{2}$,

c $F = 3x^2 + e^{-2x}$ $x_1 = 1, x_2 = 3$,

d $F = \dfrac{3}{x} + \dfrac{2}{x - 1}$ $x_1 = 2, x_2 = 4$.

8 A particle P of mass $1.5\,\text{kg}$ is moving in a straight line. The particle is initially at rest at a point O on the line. At time t seconds (where $t \geqslant 0$) the force acting on P has magnitude $(3t + 8)\,\text{N}$ and acts in the direction OP. When $t = T$, P has speed $75\,\text{m\,s}^{-1}$. Calculate

a the magnitude of the impulse exerted by the force between the times $t = 1$ and $t = 4$,

b the speed of P when $t = 3$,

c the value of T.

9 A particle of mass 0.6 kg moves in a straight line through a fixed point O. At time t seconds after passing through O the distance of P from O is x metres and the acceleration of P is $\frac{1}{5}(x^2 + 2x)\,\text{m s}^{-2}$.

a Write down, in terms of x, an expression for the force acting on P.

b Calculate the work done by the force in moving P from $x = 0$ to $x = 4$.

3.2 You can use Newton's law of gravitation to solve problems involving a particle moving away from (or towards) the Earth's surface.

Newton's law of gravitation states:

■ **The force of attraction between two bodies of masses M_1 and M_2 is directly proportional to the product of their masses and inversely proportional to the square of the distance between them.**

This law is sometimes referred to as the inverse square law. It can be expressed mathematically by the equation

$$F = \frac{GM_1M_2}{d^2}$$

where G is a constant known as the **constant of gravitation**.

This force causes particles (and bodies) to fall to the Earth and the moon to orbit the Earth.

> The numerical value of G was first determined by Henry Cavendish in 1798. In S.I. units, G is $6.67 \times 10^{-11}\,\text{kg}^{-1}\,\text{m}^3\,\text{s}^{-2}$. Example 5 demonstrates the extremely small gravitational attraction between two everyday objects. You can ignore the gravitational force between small objects in your calculations.

Relationship between G and g

When a particle of mass m is resting on the surface of the Earth the force with which the Earth attracts the particle has magnitude mg and is directed towards the centre of the Earth. By modelling the Earth as a sphere of mass M and radius R and using Newton's law of gravitation:

$$F = \frac{GmM}{R^2}$$

and $F = mg$

so $\frac{GmM}{R^2} = mg$

and hence $G = \frac{gR^2}{M}$

> This relationship means you can answer questions involving gravity without using G explicitly.

When a particle is moving away from or towards the Earth the distance d between the two particles is changing. As the force of attraction between them is given by $F = \frac{GM_1M_2}{d^2}$, it follows that the force is a function of displacement and the methods of Section 3.1 must be used to solve problems.

Example 5

Two particles of masses 0.5 kg and 2.5 kg are 4 cm apart. Calculate the magnitude of the gravitational force between them.

$$F = \frac{GM_1M_2}{d^2}$$

$$F = \frac{6.67 \times 10^{-11} \times 0.5 \times 2.5}{0.04^2}$$

$$F = 5.210\ldots \times 10^{-8}$$

The magnitude of the gravitational force between the particles is $5.210\ldots \times 10^{-8}$ N.

Use $F = \dfrac{GM_1M_2}{d^2}$ with $G = 6.67 \times 10^{-11}$, $M_1 = 0.5$, $M_2 = 2.5$ and $d = 0.04$.

This value is so small that it can be ignored in most calculations.

Example 6

Above the Earth's surface, the magnitude of the force on a particle due to the Earth's gravitational force is inversely proportional to the square of the distance of the particle from the centre of the Earth. The acceleration due to gravity on the surface of the Earth is g and the Earth can be modelled as a sphere of radius R. A particle P of mass m is a distance $(x - R)$, (where $x \geqslant R$) above the surface of the Earth.

a Prove that the magnitude of the gravitational force acting on P is $\dfrac{mgR^2}{x^2}$.

A spacecraft S is fired vertically upwards from the surface of the Earth. When it is at a height $2R$ above the surface of the Earth its speed is $\frac{1}{2}\sqrt{gR}$. Assuming that air resistance can be ignored and the rocket's engine is turned off immediately after the rocket is fired,

b find, in terms of g and R, the speed with which S was fired.

a $F \propto \dfrac{1}{x^2}$ or $F = \dfrac{k}{x^2}$

So on the surface of the Earth $F = \dfrac{k}{R^2}$

On the surface of the Earth the magnitude of the force $= mg$.

$\therefore mg = \dfrac{k}{R^2} \Rightarrow k = mgR^2$

$\therefore$ the magnitude of the gravitational force is $\dfrac{mgR^2}{x^2}$.

The force is the weight of the particle.

b $F = ma$

$$\frac{mgR^2}{x^2} = -m\ddot{x}$$

Use $F = ma$ with the information found in **a** about the force.

$$v\frac{dv}{dx} = -\frac{gR^2}{x^2}$$

The force is a function of x so replace $\ddot{x}$ with $v\frac{dv}{dx}$.

$$\int v\,dv = -gR^2\int\frac{1}{x^2}\,dx$$

$$\frac{1}{2}v^2 = gR^2\frac{1}{x} + C$$

Separate the variables and integrate. Don't forget to include the constant of integration.

$$x = 3R, v = \frac{1}{2}\sqrt{gR}$$

$$\Rightarrow \frac{1}{2} \times \frac{1}{4}gR = gR^2 \times \frac{1}{3R} + C$$

$$C = -\frac{5}{24}gR$$

Use the information in the question to obtain the value of C.

$$\frac{1}{2}v^2 = gR^2\frac{1}{x} - \frac{5}{24}gR$$

$$x = R \Rightarrow \frac{1}{2}v^2 = gR^2 \times \frac{1}{R} - \frac{5}{24}gR = \frac{19}{24}gR$$

Finally make $x = R$ and obtain an expression for v as required.

$$\therefore S \text{ is fired with speed } \sqrt{\left(\frac{19}{12}gR\right)}.$$

Exercise 3B

Whenever a numerical value of g is required, take $g = 9.8\,\text{m s}^{-2}$.

1 Above the Earth's surface, the magnitude of the force on a particle due to the Earth's gravitational force is inversely proportional to the square of the distance of the particle from the centre of the Earth. The acceleration due to gravity on the surface of the Earth is g and the Earth can be modelled as a sphere of radius R. A particle P of mass m is a distance $(x - R)$ (where $x \geq R$) above the surface of the Earth. Prove that the magnitude of the gravitational force acting on P is $\frac{mgR^2}{x^2}$.

2 The Earth can be modelled as a sphere of radius R. At a distance x (where $x \geq R$) from the centre of the Earth the magnitude of the acceleration due to the Earth's gravitational force is A. On the surface of the Earth, the magnitude of the acceleration due to the Earth's gravitational force is g. Prove that $A = \frac{gR^2}{x^2}$.

In questions 3 to 6 you may assume either of the results proved in questions 1 and 2.

3 A spacecraft S is fired vertically upwards from the surface of the Earth. When it is at a height R, where R is the radius of the Earth, above the surface of the Earth its speed is $\sqrt{gR}$. Model the spacecraft as a particle and the Earth as a sphere of radius R and find, in terms of g and R, the speed with which S was fired. (You may assume that air resistance can be ignored and that the rocket's engine is turned off immediately after the rocket is fired.)

4 A rocket of mass m is fired vertically upwards from the surface of the Earth with initial speed U. The Earth is modelled as a sphere of radius R and the rocket as a particle. Find an expression for the speed of the rocket when it has travelled a distance X metres. (You may assume that air resistance can be ignored and that the rocket's engine is turned off immediately after the rocket is fired.)

5 A particle is fired vertically upwards from the Earth's surface. The initial speed of the particle is u where $u^2 = 3gR$ and R is the radius of the Earth. Find, in terms of g and R, the speed of the particle when it is at a height $4R$ above the Earth's surface. (You may assume that air resistance can be ignored.)

6 A particle is moving in a straight line towards the centre of the Earth, which is assumed to be a sphere of radius R. The particle starts from rest when its distance from the centre of the Earth is $3R$. Find the speed of the particle as it hits the surface of the Earth. (You may assume that air resistance can be ignored.)

3.3 You can solve problems about a particle which is moving in a straight line with simple harmonic motion.

■ Simple harmonic motion (S.H.M.) is motion in which the acceleration of a particle P is always towards a fixed point O on the line of motion of P. The magnitude of the acceleration is proportional to the displacement of P from O.

The point O is called the **centre of oscillation**.

We write $\ddot{x} = -\omega^2 x$

> The minus sign means that the acceleration is always directed towards O.
> $\ddot{x}$ is always in the direction of *increasing* x.

This can be shown on a diagram

As $\ddot{x}$ is a function of x, we use $\ddot{x} = v\dfrac{dv}{dx}$

$$v\frac{dv}{dx} = -\omega^2 x$$

$$\int v\,dv = \int -\omega^2 x\,dx$$

> Separate the variables and integrate.

$$\tfrac{1}{2}v^2 = -\omega^2 \times \tfrac{1}{2}x^2 + C$$

> C is the constant of integration.

The speed of P is the modulus of v or the modulus of $\dfrac{dx}{dt}$ $\left(\text{as } v = \dfrac{dx}{dt}\right)$.

This speed is zero when x has its maximum or minimum value.
Let the maximum displacement of P from O be a. This gives:

$$0 = -\omega^2 \times \tfrac{1}{2}a^2 + C$$

$$C = \tfrac{1}{2}\omega^2 a^2$$

Hence $\qquad \frac{1}{2}v^2 = -\frac{1}{2}\omega^2 x^2 + \frac{1}{2}\omega^2 a^2$

or $\qquad v^2 = \omega^2(a^2 - x^2)$

This is a standard result which should be memorised. It may be quoted and used in the examination without proof.

The displacement, x, can now be found by replacing v with $\frac{dx}{dt}$ and integrating.

$$v = \pm\omega(a^2 - x^2)^{\frac{1}{2}}$$

$$\frac{dx}{dt} = \pm\omega(a^2 - x^2)^{\frac{1}{2}}$$

Separating the variables and integrating:

$$\int \frac{dx}{(a^2 - x^2)^{\frac{1}{2}}} = \pm \int \omega \, dt$$

The left hand integral needs a substitution, as shown in book C4, Section 6.6.

Substitute $\qquad x = a \sin \theta$

$$dx \equiv a \cos \theta \, d\theta$$

$$(a^2 - x^2)^{\frac{1}{2}} = (a^2 - a^2 \sin^2 \theta)^{\frac{1}{2}} = a \cos \theta \quad\longleftarrow\quad \text{Use } \cos^2 \theta + \sin^2 \theta = 1.$$

$$\int \frac{dx}{(a^2 - x^2)^{\frac{1}{2}}} = \int \frac{a \cos \theta}{a \cos \theta} d\theta = \int d\theta$$

So $\qquad \int d\theta = \pm \int \omega \, dt$

$\qquad\qquad \theta = \pm\omega t + \alpha \quad\longleftarrow\quad$ α is the constant of integration.

and $\qquad \sin \theta = \sin(\omega t + \alpha)$

$\qquad\qquad x = a \sin(\omega t + \alpha) \quad\longleftarrow\quad$ The substitution must be reversed to find x.

This is a periodic function with maximum and minimum values $\pm a$ and period $\frac{2\pi}{\omega}$.

a is the **amplitude** of the motion and $-a \leqslant x \leqslant a$.

We can use different values of α to investigate the motion further.

Case (i) $\alpha = 0$

The above equation, $x = a \sin(\omega t + \alpha)$
becomes $x = a \sin \omega t$.
Here is the graph of $x = a \sin \omega t$:

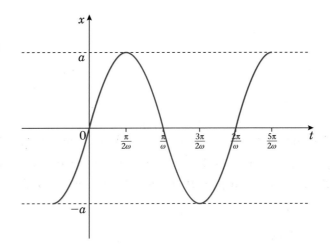

As the graph passes through the origin, we have $x = 0$ when $t = 0$. Thus $x = a \sin \omega t$ gives the displacement from the centre of oscillation of a particle moving with S.H.M. of amplitude a and period $\frac{2\pi}{\omega}$ which is at the centre of the oscillation when $t = 0$.

Case (ii) $\alpha = \dfrac{\pi}{2}$

This time the equation, $x = a \sin(\omega t + \alpha)$ becomes $x = a \sin\left(\omega t + \frac{\pi}{2}\right)$.

Your knowledge of transformations of graphs (see book C1, Chapter 4) tells you that the graph of $x = a \sin\left(\omega t + \frac{\pi}{2}\right)$ is the same shape as the graph of $x = a \sin \omega t$ but is translated $\frac{\pi}{2}$ to the left. Hence the graph of $x = a \sin\left(\omega t + \frac{\pi}{2}\right)$ is:

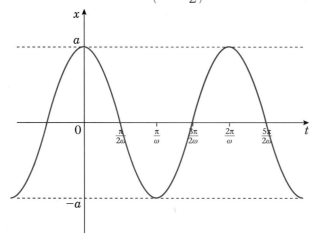

This is also the graph of $x = a \cos \omega t$. When $t = 0$ the particle's displacement from O is a.

Once again, the amplitude is a and the period is $\frac{2\pi}{\omega}$.

Case (iii) α is neither of the above.

This time the graph of $x = a \sin(\omega t + \alpha)$ is a translation of the graph of $x = a \sin \omega t$ through a distance α to the left:

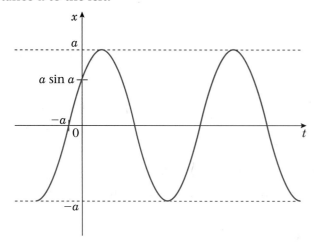

The particle is neither at the centre nor at an extreme point of the oscillation when $t = 0$.

■ For S.H.M. of amplitude a defined by the equation $\ddot{x} = -\omega^2 x$
  - $v^2 = \omega^2(a^2 - x^2)$
  - If P is at the centre of the oscillation when $t = 0$, use $x = a \sin \omega t$
  - If P is at an end point of the oscillation when $t = 0$, use $x = a \cos \omega t$
  - If P is at some other point when $t = 0$, use $x = a \sin(\omega t + \alpha)$

Questions set in the M3 examination can be solved by using $x = a \sin \omega t$ or $x = a \cos \omega t$ as appropriate.

Geometrical methods

You can also use a geometrical method to solve a simple harmonic motion problem.

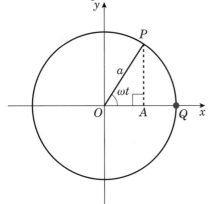

A particle P is moving round a circle of radius a, centre the origin O. The particle has a constant angular speed ω in an anticlockwise sense. (There is more about angular speed and motion in a circle in Chapter 4.) The foot of the perpendicular from P to the x-axis is the point A.

The motion is timed from the instant when P is at the point Q on the x-axis. So t seconds later, $\angle POA = \omega t$ and $OA = x = a \cos \omega t$.

Hence $\dot{x} = -a\omega \sin \omega t$

and $\ddot{x} = -a\omega^2 \cos \omega t = -\omega^2 x$

This shows that the point A is moving along the x-axis with simple harmonic motion.

The amplitude is a and the period is $\dfrac{2\pi}{\omega}$.

The circle associated with any particular simple harmonic motion is called the **reference circle.** Using the reference circle can be useful when calculating the time taken for a particle to move between two points of the oscillation, as shown in Example 11.

Example 7

A particle is moving along a straight line with S.H.M. The amplitude of the motion is 0.8 m. It passes through the centre of the oscillation O with speed $2 \, \text{m s}^{-1}$. Calculate

a the period of the oscillation,

b the speed of the particle when it is 0.4 m from O,

c the time the particle takes to travel 0.4 m from O.

a $v^2 = \omega^2(a^2 - x^2)$

$2^2 = \omega^2(0.8^2 - 0)$

> Use $v^2 = \omega^2(a^2 - x^2)$ with $v = 2$, $a = 0.8$ and $x = 0$.

$\omega = \dfrac{2}{0.8} = 2.5$

> Solve for ω.

$\text{period} = \dfrac{2\pi}{\omega}$

$= \dfrac{2\pi}{2.5} = \dfrac{4\pi}{5}$

> Use $\text{period} = \dfrac{2\pi}{\omega}$ with $\omega = 2.5$.

The period is $\dfrac{4\pi}{5}$ s.

b $v^2 = \omega^2(a^2 - x^2)$

$v^2 = 2.5^2(0.8^2 - 0.4^2)$

> Use $v^2 = \omega^2(a^2 - x^2)$ with $\omega = 2.5$, $a = 0.8$ and $x = 0.4$ and solve for v.

$v = 1.732...$

The particle's speed is 1.73 m s^{-1} (3 s.f.).

c $x = a \sin \omega t$

$0.4 = 0.8 \sin 2.5t$

> Take $t = 0$ at the centre and use $x = a \sin \omega t$ with $\omega = 2.5$, $a = 0.8$ and $x = 0.4$.

$\sin 2.5t = 0.5$

$2.5t = \sin^{-1} 0.5$

$t = \dfrac{1}{2.5} \sin^{-1} 0.5 = 0.2094...$

> Remember to have your calculator in radian mode.

The particle takes 0.209 s (3 s.f.).

Example 8

A particle P of mass 0.5 kg is moving along a straight line. At time t seconds, the distance of P from a fixed point O on the line is x metres. The force acting on P has magnitude $10x$ and acts in the direction PO.

a Show that P is moving with simple harmonic motion.

b Find the period of the motion.

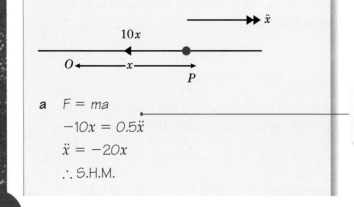

a $F = ma$

$-10x = 0.5\ddot{x}$

> To establish S.H.M., the equation of motion must reduce to the form $\ddot{x} = -\omega^2 x$.
> $\ddot{x}$ is always in the direction of increasing x.

$\ddot{x} = -20x$

$\therefore$ S.H.M.

b $\ddot{x} = -20x$

$\therefore \omega = \sqrt{20}$

Period $= \dfrac{2\pi}{\omega} = \dfrac{2\pi}{\sqrt{20}}$

$= \dfrac{\pi}{\sqrt{5}}\,s$

> Compare the equation for P found in **a** with $\ddot{x} = -\omega^2 x$ to find ω.

> The answer can be left in its exact form or given correct to 3 s.f. (1.40 s).

Example 9

A particle is moving in a straight line with simple harmonic motion. Its maximum acceleration is $12\,\text{m s}^{-2}$ and its maximum speed is $4\,\text{m s}^{-1}$. Calculate

a the period of the motion,

b the amplitude of the motion.

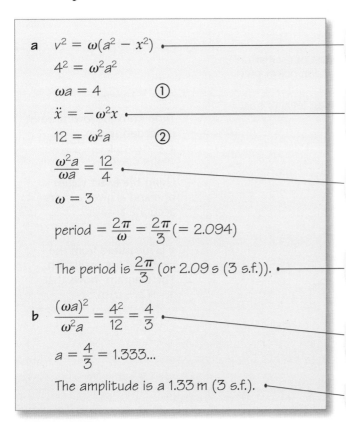

a $v^2 = \omega(a^2 - x^2)$

$4^2 = \omega^2 a^2$

$\omega a = 4 \qquad ①$

$\ddot{x} = -\omega^2 x$

$12 = \omega^2 a \qquad ②$

$\dfrac{\omega^2 a}{\omega a} = \dfrac{12}{4}$

$\omega = 3$

period $= \dfrac{2\pi}{\omega} = \dfrac{2\pi}{3}(= 2.094)$

The period is $\dfrac{2\pi}{3}$ (or 2.09 s (3 s.f.)).

b $\dfrac{(\omega a)^2}{\omega^2 a} = \dfrac{4^2}{12} = \dfrac{4}{3}$

$a = \dfrac{4}{3} = 1.333...$

The amplitude is a 1.33 m (3 s.f.).

> As $v^2 = \omega^2(a^2 - x^2)$, v is maximum when $x = 0$.

> As $\ddot{x} = -\omega^2 x$, and hence $|\ddot{x}| = |-\omega^2 x| = \omega^2 |x|$ acceleration is maximum when $|x| = a$.

> Divide equation ② by equation ① to find ω.

> Unless you are told the accuracy required, give the exact answer.

> Square equation ① and divide by equation ② to find a.

> The exact answer, $\frac{4}{3}$ or $1\frac{1}{3}$ is acceptable.

Example 10

A small rowing boat is floating on the surface of the sea, tied to a pier. The boat moves up and down in a vertical line and it can be modelled as a particle moving with simple harmonic motion. The boat takes 2 s to travel directly from its highest point, which is 3 m below the pier, to its lowest point. The maximum speed of the boat is $3\,\text{m s}^{-1}$. Calculate

a the amplitude of the motion,

b the time taken by the boat to rise from its lowest point to a point 5 m below the pier.

a Period $= \dfrac{2\pi}{\omega} = 4$

> The time taken from the highest point to the lowest point is half the period.

$$\therefore \omega = \frac{2\pi}{4} = \frac{\pi}{2}$$

$$v^2 = \omega^2(a^2 - x^2)$$

$$3^2 = \left(\frac{\pi}{2}\right)^2 (a^2 - 0)$$

$$a^2 = 3^2 \times \left(\frac{2}{\pi}\right)^2$$

$$a = \frac{6}{\pi} = 1.909\ldots$$

The amplitude is 1.91 m (3 s.f.).

b

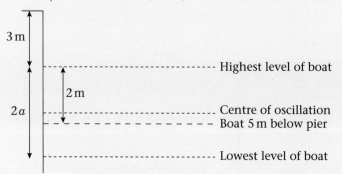

3 m

2 m

2a

Highest level of boat

Centre of oscillation
Boat 5 m below pier

Lowest level of boat

$$x = a\cos\omega t$$

> Time from the lowest point is needed so use $x = a\cos\omega t$.

$$x = \frac{6}{\pi}\cos\left(\frac{\pi}{2}t\right)$$

> Using the exact values of a and ω gives a more accurate answer.

$$2 - \frac{6}{\pi} = \frac{6}{\pi}\cos\left(\frac{\pi}{2}t\right)$$

> x is measured from the centre of the oscillation. The diagram shows that $x = (2 - a)$ m.

$$\cos\left(\frac{\pi}{2}t\right) = \frac{\pi}{6} \times \left(2 - \frac{6}{\pi}\right)$$

$$\frac{\pi}{2}t = 1.523\ldots$$

$$t = \frac{2}{\pi} \times 1.523\ldots = 0.9699\ldots$$

The time taken is 0.970 s (3 s.f.).

Example 11

A particle P is moving with simple harmonic motion along a straight line. The centre of the oscillation is the point O, the amplitude is 0.6 m and the period is 8 s. The points A and B are points on the line of P's motion and are on opposite sides of O. The distance OA is 0.5 m and OB is 0.1 m. Calculate the time taken by P to move directly from A to B.

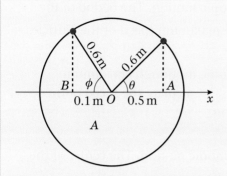

As P moves from A to B, the point on the circle moves round an arc of the circle which subtends an angle of $(\pi - \theta - \phi)^c$ at O.

$$\theta = \cos^{-1}\left(\frac{0.5}{0.6}\right) = \cos^{-1}\left(\frac{5}{6}\right)$$

$$\phi = \cos^{-1}\left(\frac{0.1}{0.6}\right) = \cos^{-1}\left(\frac{1}{6}\right)$$

Use the diagram to find θ and ϕ. Keep the exact forms.

$$\text{Time} = \frac{(\pi - \theta - \phi)}{2\pi} \times 8$$

$$= \frac{\pi - \cos^{-1}\left(\frac{5}{6}\right) - \cos^{-1}\left(\frac{1}{6}\right)}{2\pi} \times 8$$

$$= 1.467\ldots$$

The period is 8 s. This corresponds to an angle of 2π at the centre. We use proportion to find the time we require.

The time to travel from A to B is 1.47 s (3 s.f.).

Exercise 3C

1 A particle P is moving in a straight line with simple harmonic motion. The amplitude of the oscillation is 0.5 m and P passes through the centre of the oscillation O with speed $2\,\text{m s}^{-1}$. Calculate

a the period of the oscillation,

b the speed of P when $OP = 0.2\,\text{m}$.

2 A particle P is moving in a straight line with simple harmonic motion. The period is $\frac{\pi}{3}$ s and P's maximum speed is $6\,\text{m s}^{-1}$. The centre of the oscillation is O. Calculate

a the amplitude of the motion,

b the speed of P 0.3 s after passing through O.

3 A particle is moving in a straight line with simple harmonic motion. Its maximum speed is $10\,\text{m s}^{-1}$ and its maximum acceleration is $20\,\text{m s}^{-2}$. Calculate

a the amplitude of the motion,

b the period of the motion.

4 A particle is moving in a straight line with simple harmonic motion. The period of the motion is $\frac{3\pi}{5}$ s and the amplitude is 0.4 m. Calculate the maximum speed of the particle.

5 A particle is moving in a straight line with simple harmonic motion. Its maximum acceleration is $15\,\mathrm{m\,s^{-2}}$ and its maximum speed is $18\,\mathrm{m\,s^{-1}}$. Calculate the speed of the particle when it is 2.5 m from the centre of the oscillation.

6 A particle P is moving in a straight line with simple harmonic motion. The centre of the oscillation is O and the period is $\frac{\pi}{2}$ s. When $OP = 1.2\,\mathrm{m}$, P has speed $1.5\,\mathrm{m\,s^{-1}}$.

   a Find the amplitude of the motion.

   At time t seconds the displacement of P from O is x metres. When $t = 0$, P is passing through O.

   b Find an expression for x in terms of t.

7 A particle is moving in a straight line with simple harmonic motion. The particle performs 6 complete oscillations per second and passes through the centre of the oscillation, O, with speed $5\,\mathrm{m\,s^{-1}}$. When P passes through the point A the magnitude of P's acceleration is $20\,\mathrm{m\,s^{-1}}$. Calculate

   a the amplitude of the motion,

   b the distance OA.

8 A particle P is moving on a straight line with simple harmonic motion between two points A and B. The mid-point of AB is O. When $OP = 0.6\,\mathrm{m}$, the speed of P is $3\,\mathrm{m\,s^{-1}}$ and when $OP = 0.2\,\mathrm{m}$ the speed of P is $6\,\mathrm{m\,s^{-1}}$. Find

   a the distance AB,

   b the period of the motion.

9 A particle is moving in a straight line with simple harmonic motion. When the particle is 1 m from the centre of the oscillation, O, its speed is $0.1\,\mathrm{m\,s^{-1}}$. The period of the motion is 2π seconds. Calculate

   a the maximum speed of the particle,

   b the speed of the particle when it is 0.4 m from O.

10 A piston of mass 1.2 kg is moving with simple harmonic motion inside a cylinder. The distance between the end points of the motion is 2.5 m and the piston is performing 30 complete oscillations per minute. Calculate the maximum value of the kinetic energy of the piston.

11 A marker buoy is moving in a vertical line with simple harmonic motion. The buoy rises and falls through a distance of 0.8 m and takes 2 s for each complete oscillation. Calculate

   a the maximum speed of the buoy,

   b the time taken for the buoy to fall a distance 0.6 m from its highest point.

12 Points *O*, *A* and *B* lie in that order in a straight line. A particle *P* is moving on the line with simple harmonic motion. The motion has period 2 s and amplitude 0.5 m. The point *O* is the centre of the oscillation, *OA* = 0.2 m and *OB* = 0.3 m. Calculate the time taken by *P* to move directly from *A* to *B*.

13 A particle *P* is moving along the *x*-axis. At time *t* seconds the displacement, *x* metres, of *P* from the origin *O* is given by $x = 4 \sin 2t$.

   a Prove that *P* is moving with simple harmonic motion.

   b Write down the amplitude and period of the motion.

   c Calculate the maximum speed of *P*.

   d Calculate the least value of *t* ($t > 0$) for which *P*'s speed is 4 m s^{-1}.

   e Calculate the least value of *t* ($t > 0$) for which $x = 2$.

14 A particle *P* is moving along the *x*-axis. At time *t* seconds the displacement, *x* metres, of *P* from the origin *O* is given by $x = 3 \sin\left(4t + \frac{1}{2}\right)$.

   a Prove that *P* is moving with simple harmonic motion.

   b Write down the amplitude and period of the motion.

   c Calculate the value of *x* when $t = 0$.

   d Calculate the value of *t* ($t > 0$) the first time *P* passes through *O*.

15 On a certain day, low tide in a harbour is at 10 a.m. and the depth of the water is 5 m. High tide on the same day is at 4.15 p.m. and the water is then 15 m deep. A ship which needs a depth of water of 7 m needs to enter the harbour. Assuming that the water can be modelled as rising and falling with simple harmonic motion, calculate

   a the earliest time, to the nearest minute, after 10 a.m. at which the ship can enter the harbour,

   b the time by which the ship must leave.

16 Points *A*, *O* and *B* lie in that order in a straight line. A particle *P* is moving on the line with simple harmonic motion with centre *O*. The period of the motion is 4 s and the amplitude is 0.75 m. The distance *OA* is 0.4 m and *AB* is 0.9 m. Calculate the time taken by *P* to move directly from *B* to *A*.

3.4 **You can investigate the motion of a particle which is attached to an elastic spring or string and is oscillating in a horizontal line.**

If an elastic spring has one end attached to a fixed point *A* of a smooth horizontal surface a particle *P* can be attached to the free end. When *P* is pulled away from *A* and released *P* will move towards *A*.

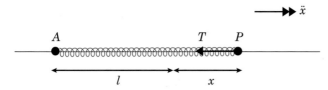

Hooke's law: $T = \dfrac{\lambda x}{l}$

See chapter 2. λ is the modulus of elasticity of the spring and l is its natural length.

$F = ma$

$-T = m\ddot{x}$

The acceleration $\ddot{x}$ is always in the direction of *increasing* x.

$m\ddot{x} = -\dfrac{\lambda x}{l}$

$\ddot{x} = -\dfrac{\lambda}{ml}x$

λ, m and l are all positive constants, so the equation is of the form $\ddot{x} = -\omega^2 x$.

So P is moving with S.H.M.

The initial extension is the maximum value of x, so is the same as the amplitude.

When the particle is attached to a **spring**, the particle will perform complete oscillations because there will always be a force acting – a tension when the spring is stretched and a thrust when the spring is compressed. The centre of the oscillation is where the tension is zero; that is the point when the spring has returned to its natural length.

When the particle is attached to a **string**, the particle will move with S.H.M. only while the string is taut. Once the string becomes slack there is no tension and the particle continues to move with constant speed until the string becomes taut again. This will happen on the far side of A from the starting point of P at a distance l from A, where l is the natural length of the string.

■ **For a particle moving on a smooth horizontal surface attached to one end of an elastic spring**
  • **the particle will move with S.H.M.**
  • **the particle will perform complete oscillations.**

■ **For a particle moving on a smooth horizontal surface attached to one end of an elastic string**
  • **the particle will move with S.H.M. while the string is taut**
  • **the particle will move with constant speed while the string is slack.**

■ **To solve problems involving elastic springs and strings**
  • **use Hooke's law to find the tension**
  • **use $F = ma$ to obtain ω**
  • **use information given in the question to obtain the amplitude.**

Sometimes the particle is attached to two springs or strings which are stretched between two fixed points. When this happens you will need to find the tensions in both the springs or strings.

Example 12

A particle P of mass $0.6\,\text{kg}$ rests on a smooth horizontal floor attached to one end of a light elastic string of natural length $0.8\,\text{m}$ and modulus of elasticity $16\,\text{N}$. The other end of the string is fixed to a point A on the floor. The particle is pulled away from A until AP measures $1.2\,\text{m}$ and released.

a Show that, while the string remains taut, P moves with simple harmonic motion.

b Calculate the speed of P when the string returns to its natural length.

c Calculate the time that elapses between the point where the string becomes slack and the point where it next becomes taut.

d Calculate the time taken by the particle to return to its starting point for the first time.

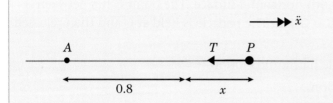

a $T = \dfrac{\lambda x}{l}$

$T = \dfrac{16x}{0.8} = 20x$

> Use Hooke's law with $l = 16$ and $l = 0.8$ to find the tension.

$F = ma$

$20x = -0.6\ddot{x}$

$\ddot{x} = -\dfrac{20}{0.6}x = -\dfrac{100}{3}x$

> Use $F = ma$ with $F = T = 20x$ and $m = 0.6$. Remember that $\ddot{x}$ is in the direction of increasing x.

The particle is moving with S.H.M.

> The equation reduces to the form $\ddot{x} = -\omega^2 x$, so S.H.M is proved.

b $\ddot{x} = -\dfrac{100}{3}x$

$\omega^2 = \dfrac{100}{3}$

> Compare the equation obtained in **a** with $\ddot{x} = -\omega^2 x$ to find ω^2.

$v^2 = \omega^2(a^2 - x^2)$

$v^2 = \dfrac{100}{3} \times 0.4^2$

> The amplitude is the same as the initial extension and at the natural length $x = 0$.

$v = 2.309\ldots$

At the natural length P has speed $2.31\,\text{m s}^{-1}$ (3 s.f.).

c The particle now moves a distance $1.6\,\text{m}$ at $2.309\ldots\,\text{m s}^{-1}$.

> The particle moves at a constant speed while the string is slack.

Time taken $= \dfrac{1.6}{2.309\ldots} = 0.6928\ldots$

The string is slack for $0.693\,\text{s}$ (3 s.f.).

d Period of the S.H.M. $= \dfrac{2\pi}{\omega} = 2\pi \times \sqrt{\dfrac{3}{100}} = 1.088\ldots$

> The particle moves through a complete oscillation and sections of constant speed (when the string is slack).

Total time $= 1.088\ldots + 2 \times 0.6928\ldots = 2.473\ldots$

The time taken is $2.47\,\text{s}$ (3 s.f.).

Example 13

A particle P of mass 0.8 kg is attached to the ends of two identical light elastic springs of natural length 1.6 m and modulus of elasticity 16 N. The free ends of the springs are attached to two points A and B which are 4 m apart on a smooth horizontal surface. The point C lies between A and B such that ABC is a straight line and $AC = 2.4$ m. The particle is held at C and then released from rest.

a Show that the subsequent motion is simple harmonic motion.

b Find the period and amplitude of the motion.

c Calculate the maximum speed of P.

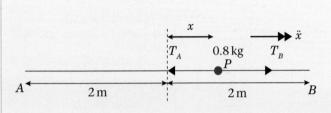

a $T = \dfrac{\lambda x}{l}$

$T_A = \dfrac{16(0.4 + x)}{1.6}$

$T_B = \dfrac{16(0.4 - x)}{1.6}$

$F = ma$

$T_B - T_A = 0.8\ddot{x}$

$\dfrac{16(0.4 - x)}{1.6} - \dfrac{16(0.4 + x)}{1.6} = 0.8\ddot{x}$

$-2 \times \dfrac{16x}{1.6} = 0.8\ddot{x}$

$\ddot{x} = -2 \times \dfrac{16x}{1.6 \times 0.8} = -25x$

The motion is S.H.M.

b $\ddot{x} = -25x$

$\omega^2 = 25, \ \omega = 5$

$\text{Period} = \dfrac{2\pi}{\omega} = \dfrac{2\pi}{5}\,\text{s}$

$\text{Amplitude} = 0.4\,\text{m}$

c $v^2 = \omega^2(a^2 - x^2)$

$v^2_{max} = 25 \times 0.4^2$

$v_{max} = 5 \times 0.4 = 2$

P's maximum speed is $2\,\text{m s}^{-1}$.

> Use Hooke's law to find the tensions in each spring. Use your diagram to work out the extensions.

> Use $F = ma$ to form an equation of motion for P. Reduce this to the form $\ddot{x} = -\omega^2 x$ to establish S.H.M.

> Compare the equation found in **a** with $\ddot{x} = -\omega^2 x$ to find ω.

> You can give an exact value or a 3 s.f. answer (1.26 s) for the period.

> As the springs are identical the centre of the oscillation is at the mid-point of AB.

Exercise 3D

1 A particle P of mass 0.5 kg is attached to one end of a light elastic spring of natural length 0.6 m and modulus of elasticity 60 N. The other end of the spring is fixed to a point A on the smooth horizontal surface on which P rests. The particle is held at rest with $AP = 0.9$ m and then released.

    a Show that P moves with simple harmonic motion.

    b Find the period and amplitude of the motion.

    c Calculate the maximum speed of P.

2 A particle P of mass 0.8 kg is attached to one end of a light elastic string of natural length 1.6 m and modulus of elasticity 20 N. The other end of the string is fixed to a point O on the smooth horizontal surface on which P rests. The particle is held at rest with $OP = 2.6$ m and then released.

    a Show that, while the string is taut, P moves with simple harmonic motion.

    b Calculate the time from the instant of release until P returns to its starting point for the first time.

3 A particle P of mass 0.4 kg is attached to one end of a light elastic string of modulus of elasticity 24 N and natural length 1.2 m. The other end of the string is fixed to a point A on the smooth horizontal table on which P rests. Initially P is at rest with $AP = 1$ m. The particle receives an impulse of magnitude 1.8 N s in the direction AP.

    a Show that, while the string is taut, P moves with simple harmonic motion.

    b Calculate the time that elapses between the moment P receives the impulse and the next time the string becomes slack.

    The particle comes to instantaneous rest for the first time at the point B.

    c Calculate the distance AB.

4 A particle P of mass 0.8 kg is attached to one end of a light elastic spring of natural length 1.2 m and modulus of elasticity 80 N. The other end of the spring is fixed to a point O on the smooth horizontal surface on which P rests. The particle is held at rest with $OP = 0.6$ m and then released.

    a Show that P moves with simple harmonic motion.

    b Find the period and amplitude of the motion.

    c Calculate the maximum speed of P.

5 A particle P of mass 0.6 kg is attached to one end of a light elastic spring of modulus of elasticity 72 N and natural length 1.2 m. The other end of the spring is fixed to a point A on the smooth horizontal table on which P rests. Initially P is at rest with $AP = 1.2$ m. The particle receives an impulse of magnitude 3 N s in the direction AP. Given that t seconds after the impulse the displacement of P from its initial position is x metres

    a find an equation for x in terms of t,

    b calculate the maximum magnitude of the acceleration of P.

6 A particle of mass 0.9 kg rests on a smooth horizontal surface attached to one end of a light elastic string of natural length 1.5 m and modulus of elasticity 24 N. The other end of the string is attached to a point on the surface. The particle is pulled so that the string measures 2 m and released from rest.

a State the amplitude of the resulting oscillation.

b Calculate the speed of the particle when the string becomes slack.

Before the string becomes taut again the particle hits a vertical surface which is at right angles to the particle's direction of motion. The coefficient of restitution between the particle and the vertical surface is $\frac{3}{5}$.

c Calculate **i** the period and **ii** the amplitude of the oscillation which takes place when the string becomes taut once more.

7 A smooth cylinder is fixed with its axis horizontal. A piston of mass 2.5 kg is inside the cylinder, attached to one end of the cylinder by a spring of modulus of elasticity 400 N and natural length 50 cm. The piston is held at rest in the cylinder with the spring compressed to a length of 42 cm. The piston is then released. The spring can be modelled as a light elastic spring and the piston can be modelled as a particle.

a Find the period of the resulting oscillations.

b Find the maximum value of the kinetic energy of the piston.

8 A particle P of mass 0.5 kg is attached to one end of a light elastic string of natural length 0.4 m and modulus of elasticity 30 N. The other end of the string is attached to a point on the smooth horizontal surface on which P rests. The particle is pulled until the string measures 0.6 m and then released from rest.

a Calculate the speed of P when the string becomes slack for the first time.

The string breaks at the instant when it returns to its natural length. When P has travelled a distance 0.3 m from the point of release the surface becomes rough. The coefficient of friction between P and the surface is 0.25. The particle comes to rest T seconds after it was released.

b Find the value of T.

9 A particle P of mass 0.4 kg is attached to two identical light elastic springs each of natural length 1.2 m and modulus of elasticity 12 N. The free ends of the strings are attached to points A and B which are 4 m apart on a smooth horizontal surface. The point C lies between A and B with $AC = 1.4$ m and $CB = 2.6$ m. The particle is held at C and released from rest.

a Show that P moves with simple harmonic motion.

b Calculate the maximum value of the kinetic energy of P.

10 A particle P of mass m is attached to two identical light strings of natural length l and modulus of elasticity $3mg$. The free ends of the strings are attached to fixed points A and B which are $5l$ apart on a smooth horizontal surface. The particle is held at the point C, where $AC = l$ and A, B and C lie on a straight line, and is then released from rest.

a Show that P moves with simple harmonic motion.

b Find the period of the motion.

c Write down the amplitude of the motion.

d Find the speed of P when $AP = 3l$.

11 A light elastic string has natural length 2.5 m and modulus of elasticity 15 N. A particle P of mass 0.5 kg is attached to the string at the point K where K divides the unstretched string in the ratio $2:3$. The ends of the string are then attached to the points A and B which are 5 m apart on a smooth horizontal surface. The particle is then pulled aside and held at rest in contact with the surface at the point C where $AC = 3$ m and ACB is a straight line. The particle is then released from rest.

a Show that P moves with simple harmonic motion of period $\frac{\pi}{5}\sqrt{2}$.

b Find the amplitude of the motion.

3.5 **You can investigate the motion of a particle which is attached to an elastic spring or string and is oscillating in a vertical line.**

A particle which is hanging in equilibrium attached to one end of an elastic spring or string, the other end of which is fixed, can be pulled downwards and released. The particle will then oscillate in a vertical line about its equilibrium position.

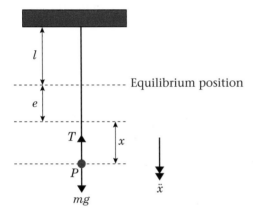

When the particle is a distance x below its equilibrium position its acceleration is $\ddot{x}$ away from the equilibrium position.

At the equilibrium position, the tension in the spring or string is mg.
Using Hooke's law:

$$T = \frac{\lambda \times \text{extension}}{l}$$

$$mg = \frac{\lambda e}{l}$$

> λ is the modulus of elasticity and l is the natural length of the spring or string. e is the extension of the spring or string in the equilibrium position.

$$e = \frac{mgl}{\lambda}$$

Now consider the particle at a distance x below its equilibrium position.

$$T = \lambda \times \frac{\text{extension}}{l}$$

$$T = \frac{\lambda(x + e)}{l}$$

> The particle is a distance x below the equilibrium position, so the extension is $x + e$.

$$T = \frac{\lambda\left(x + \frac{mgl}{\lambda}\right)}{l} = \frac{\lambda x}{l} + mg$$

$$F = ma$$
$$mg - T = m\ddot{x}$$

When using $F = ma$ the weight of the particle must be included as well as the tension.

$$mg - \left(\frac{\lambda x}{l} + mg\right) = m\ddot{x}$$

$$-\frac{\lambda x}{l} = m\ddot{x}$$

$$\ddot{x} = -\frac{\lambda}{ml}x$$

λ, m and l are all positive constants, so the equation is of the form $\ddot{x} = -\omega^2 x$. It is the same result as obtained for a horizontal oscillation.

The particle is moving with S.H.M.

As in the case of horizontal oscillations, a particle attached to one end of a spring will perform complete oscillations. If the particle is attached to one end of an elastic string it will only move with S.H.M. while the string is taut. If the amplitude is greater than the extension at the equilibrium position the string will become slack before the particle reaches the upper end of the oscillation. Once the string becomes slack the oscillatory motion ceases and the particle moves freely under gravity until it falls back to the position where the string is once again taut.

- **For a particle hanging in equilibrium attached to one end of an elastic spring and displaced vertically from its equilibrium position**
  - **the particle will move with S.H.M.**
  - **the particle will perform complete oscillations**
  - **the centre of the oscillation will be the equilibrium position.**

- **For a particle hanging in equilibrium attached to one end of an elastic string and displaced vertically from its equilibrium position**
  - **the particle will move with S.H.M. while the string is taut**
  - **the particle will perform complete oscillations if the amplitude is no greater than the equilibrium extension**
  - **if the amplitude is greater than the equilibrium extension the particle will move freely under gravity while the string is slack.**

A particle can be attached to two springs or strings which are hanging side by side or stretched in a vertical line between two fixed points. The basic method of solution remains the same.

Example 14

A particle P of mass 1.2 kg is attached to one end of a light elastic spring of modulus of elasticity 60 N and natural length 60 cm. The other end of the spring is attached to a fixed point A on a ceiling. The particle hangs in equilibrium at the point B.

a Find the extension of the spring.

The particle is now raised vertically a distance 15 cm and released from rest.

b Prove that P will move with simple harmonic motion.

c Find the period and amplitude of the motion.

d Find the speed of P as it passes through B.

e Find the speed of P at the instant when the spring has returned to its natural length.

a

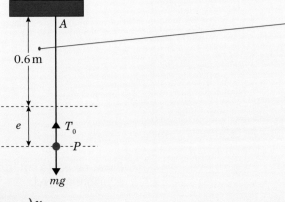

$T = \dfrac{\lambda x}{l}$

$T_0 = \dfrac{60e}{0.6}$

$1.2g = \dfrac{60e}{0.6}$

$e = \dfrac{1.2 \times 9.8 \times 0.6}{60} = 0.1176$

The extension is 0.118 m (3 s.f.) or 11.8 cm (3 s.f.).

Change cm to m.

Use Hooke's law to find the tension in terms of the extension.

At the equilibrium position the tension must equal the weight.

b

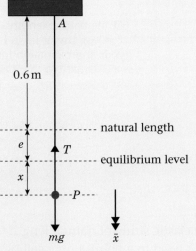

$T = \dfrac{\lambda x}{l}$

$T = \dfrac{60(x + e)}{1.2}$

$F = ma$

$mg - T = m\ddot{x}$

$mg - \dfrac{60(x + e)}{0.6} = m\ddot{x}$

$\dfrac{60e}{0.6} - \dfrac{60(x + e)}{0.6} = 1.2\ddot{x}$

$\ddot{x} = -\dfrac{60x}{1.2 \times 0.6} = -\dfrac{250}{3}x$

P moves with S.H.M.

Draw a new diagram showing P at a distance x below the equilibrium level. The acceleration, $\ddot{x}$, is in the direction of increasing x.

Use Hooke's law once more. This time the extension is $x + e$.

When you use $F = ma$ you must include the weight of the particle.

Do not use an approximation for e. Instead, use your work from **a** to replace mg with the tension at the equilibrium level in terms of e.

When you simplify the equation e vanishes.

c $\ddot{x} = -\dfrac{250}{3}x$

$\omega^2 = \dfrac{250}{3}$

$\text{period} = \dfrac{2\pi}{\omega} = \dfrac{2\pi}{\sqrt{\dfrac{250}{3}}} = 0.6882\ldots$

The period is $0.688\,s$ (3 s.f.).

The amplitude is $15\,cm$. •———— P was raised $15\,cm$ from its equilibrium level.

d $v^2 = \omega^2(a^2 - x^2)$

$v_B^2 = \dfrac{250}{3}(0.15^2 - 0)$ •———— $x = 0$ at B.

$v_B = \sqrt{\dfrac{250}{3}} \times 0.15 = 1.369\ldots$ •———— This is also the maximum speed of P.

The speed at B is $1.37\,m\,s^{-1}$ (3 s.f.).

e $v^2 = \omega^2(a^2 - x^2)$

$v^2 = \dfrac{250}{3}(0.15^2 - (-0.1176)^2)$ •———— At the natural length $x = -e$. Use at least 4 s.f. in your approximation for e.

$v = 0.8500\ldots$

The speed at the natural length is $0.850\,m\,s^{-1}$ (3 s.f.).

Example 15

A particle P of mass $0.2\,kg$ is attached to one end of a light elastic string of natural length $0.6\,m$ and modulus of elasticity $8\,N$. The other end of the string is fixed to a point A on a ceiling. When the particle is hanging in equilibrium the length of the string is $L\,m$.

a Calculate the value of L.

The particle is held at A and released from rest. It first comes to instantaneous rest when the length of the string is $K\,m$.

b Use energy considerations to calculate the value of K.

c Show that while the string is taut P is moving with simple harmonic motion.

The string becomes slack again for the first time T seconds after P was released from A.

d Calculate the value of T.

$$0.2g$$

a $T = \dfrac{\lambda x}{l}$

Use Hooke's law.

$$0.2g = \dfrac{8e}{0.6}$$

At the equilibrium position the tension must equal the weight.

$$e = \dfrac{0.2 \times 9.8 \times 0.6}{8} = 0.147$$

$$L = 0.6 + 0.147 = 0.747$$

The total length of the string is required.

b E.P.E. gained $= \dfrac{\lambda x^2}{2l}$

$$= \dfrac{8(K - 0.6)^2}{2 \times 0.6}$$

G.P.E. lost $= mgh = 0.2 \times 9.8K$

The question states that you must do this part using conservation of energy. The kinetic energy is zero at both points under consideration.

$$\dfrac{8(K - 0.6)^2}{2 \times 0.6} = 0.2 \times 9.8K$$

$$K^2 - 1.2K + 0.36 = \dfrac{2 \times 0.6 \times 0.2 \times 9.8K}{8}$$

$$K^2 - 1.2K + 0.36 = 0.294K$$

$$K^2 - 1.494K + 0.36 = 0$$

$$K = \dfrac{1.494 \pm \sqrt{1.494^2 - 4 \times 0.36}}{2}$$

$$K = 1.191 \text{ or } 0.3020$$

$$\therefore K = 1.19$$

The value of K must be greater than the natural length of the string.

c

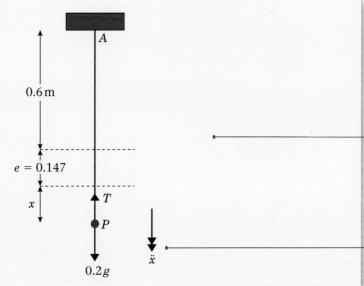

0.6 m

$e = 0.147$

x

A

T

P

$\ddot{x}$

$0.2g$

Draw a diagram which shows the natural length and the equilibrium level as well as the distance of P from the centre of the oscillation (x).

$T = \dfrac{\lambda \times \text{extension}}{l}$

$T = \dfrac{8(x + e)}{0.6}$

$F = ma$

$0.2g - \dfrac{8(x + e)}{0.6} = 0.2\ddot{x}$

$\dfrac{8e}{0.6} - \dfrac{8(x + e)}{0.6} = 0.2\ddot{x}$

$\ddot{x} = -\dfrac{8x}{0.6 \times 0.2} = -\dfrac{800}{12}x$

$\therefore$ S.H.M.

Remember that $\ddot{x}$ must be in the direction of increasing x.

There is no need to use an approximation for e as $\dfrac{8e}{0.6}$ from part **a**.

Reduce the equation of motion to the form $\ddot{x} = -\omega^2 x$ to establish S.H.M.

d Time to fall 0.6 m from rest:

$s = ut + \frac{1}{2}at^2$

$0.6 = 0 + \frac{1}{2} \times 9.8t^2$

$t^2 = \dfrac{0.6}{4.9}$

$t = 0.3499...$

For S.H.M.:

$\omega = \sqrt{\dfrac{800}{12}} = \sqrt{100 \times \dfrac{8}{12}} = 10\sqrt{\dfrac{2}{3}} = \dfrac{10\sqrt{6}}{3}$

amplitude $= K - L = 1.191 - 0.747 = 0.444$

$x = 0.444 \cos \omega t$

when $x = 0.147$, $0.147 = 0.444 \cos \omega t$

$\cos \omega t = \dfrac{0.147}{0.444}$

Until the string is taut, P is falling freely under gravity.

Because of the symmetry of S.H.M. there are several ways to obtain the time for which the string is taut. Whichever method you use you must show your working clearly.

$$t = \frac{1}{\omega}\cos^{-1}\left(\frac{0.147}{0.444}\right)$$

$$t = 0.1510\dots$$

Using $x = a\cos\omega t$ with the positive value of x when the string is at its natural length will give the time from the high point of the oscillation (if it were complete) to the point where the string becomes taut.

$$\text{Period} = \frac{2\pi}{\omega} = 2\pi \times \frac{3}{10\sqrt{6}} = 0.7695\dots$$

Time for which string is taut
$$= 0.7695 - 2 \times 0.1510 = 0.4675\dots$$

Subtracting twice the time just found from the period will give the time for which the string is taut in any one oscillation.

Total time $= 0.4675\dots + 0.3499 = 0.8174\dots$

$\therefore T = 0.817$ (3 s.f.)

Finally, add the time taken while falling freely under gravity to the time for which the string is taut.

Exercise 3E

Whenever a numerical value of g is required, take $g = 9.8\,\text{m s}^{-2}$.

1. A particle P of mass 0.75 kg is hanging in equilibrium attached to one end of a light elastic spring of natural length 1.5 m and modulus of elasticity 80 N. The other end of the spring is attached to a fixed point A vertically above P.

   a Calculate the length of the spring.

   The particle is pulled downwards and held at a point B which is vertically below A. The particle is then released from rest.

   b Show that P moves with simple harmonic motion.

   c Calculate the period of the oscillations.

   The particle passes through its equilibrium position with speed $2.5\,\text{m s}^{-1}$.

   d Calculate the amplitude of the oscillations.

2. A particle P of mass 0.5 kg is attached to the free end of a light elastic spring of natural length 0.5 m and modulus of elasticity 50 N. The other end of the spring is attached to a fixed point A and P hangs in equilibrium vertically below A.

   a Calculate the extension of the spring.

   The particle is now pulled vertically down a further 0.2 m and released from rest.

   b Calculate the period of the resulting oscillations.

   c Calculate the maximum speed of the particle.

3. A particle P of mass 2 kg is hanging in equilibrium attached to the free end of a light elastic spring of natural length 1.5 m and modulus of elasticity λ N. The other end of the spring is fixed to a point A vertically above P. The particle receives an impulse of magnitude 3 N s in the direction AP.

a Find the speed of P immediately after the impact.

b Show that P moves with simple harmonic motion.

The period of the oscillations is $\frac{\pi}{2}$ s.

c Find the value of λ.

d Find the amplitude of the oscillations.

4 A light elastic spring has one end A fixed and hangs vertically with a particle P of mass 0.6 kg attached to its free end. Initially P is hanging freely in equilibrium. The particle is then pulled vertically downwards and released from rest.

a Show that P moves with simple harmonic motion.

The period of the motion is $\frac{\pi}{5}$ s and the maximum and minimum distances of P below A are 1.2 m and 0.8 m respectively. Calculate

b the amplitude of the oscillation,

c the maximum speed of P,

d the maximum magnitude of the acceleration of P.

5 A piston of mass 2 kg moves inside a smooth cylinder which is fixed with its axis vertical. The piston is attached to the base of the cylinder by a spring of natural length 12 cm and modulus of elasticity 500 N. The piston is released from rest at a point where the spring is compressed to a length of 8 cm. Assuming that the spring can be modelled as a light elastic spring and the piston as a particle, calculate

a the period of the resulting oscillations,

b the maximum speed of the piston.

6 A light elastic string of natural length 40 cm has one end A attached to a fixed point. A particle P of mass 0.4 kg is attached to the free end of the string and hangs freely in equilibrium vertically below A. The distance AP is 45 cm.

a Find the modulus of elasticity of the string.

The particle is now pulled vertically downwards until AP measures 52 cm and then released from rest.

b Show that, while the string is taut, P moves with simple harmonic motion.

c Find the period and amplitude of the motion.

d Find the greatest speed of P during the motion.

e Find the time taken by P to rise 11 cm from the point of release.

7 A particle P of mass 0.4 kg is attached to one end of a light elastic string of natural length 0.5 m and modulus of elasticity 10 N. The other end of the string is attached to a fixed point A and P is initially hanging freely in equilibrium vertically below A. The particle is then pulled vertically downwards a further 0.2 m and released from rest.

a Calculate the time from release until the string becomes slack for the first time.

b Calculate the time between the string first becoming slack and the next time it becomes taut.

8 A particle P of mass 1.5 kg is hanging freely attached to one end of a light elastic string of natural length 1 m and modulus of elasticity 40 N. The other end of the string is attached to a fixed point A on a ceiling. The particle is pulled vertically downwards until AP is 1.8 m and released from rest. When P has risen a distance 0.4 m the string is cut.

    a Calculate the greatest height P reaches above its equilibrium position.

    b Calculate the time taken from release to reach that greatest height.

9 A particle P of mass 1.5 kg is attached to the mid-point of a light elastic string of natural length 1.2 m and modulus of elasticity 15 N. The ends of the string are fixed to the points A and B where A is vertically above B and $AB = 2.8$ m.

    a Given that P is in equilibrium calculate the length AP.

    The particle is now pulled downwards a distance 0.15 m from its equilibrium position and released from rest.

    b Prove that P moves with simple harmonic motion.

    T seconds after being released P is 0.1 m above its equilibrium position.

    c Find the value of T.

10 A rock climber of mass 70 kg is attached to one end of a rope. He falls from a ledge which is 8 m vertically below the point to which the other end of the rope is fixed. The climber falls vertically without hitting the rock face. Assuming that the climber can be modelled as a particle and the rope as a light elastic string of natural length 16 m and modulus of elasticity 40 000 N, calculate

    a the climber's speed at the instant when the rope becomes taut,

    b the maximum distance of the climber below the ledge,

    c the time from falling from the ledge to reaching his lowest point.

Mixed exercise 3F

Whenever a numerical value of g is required, take $g = 9.8 \, \mathrm{m \, s^{-2}}$.

1 A particle P is moving with simple harmonic motion between two points A and B which are 0.4 m apart on a horizontal line. The mid-point of AB is O. At time $t = 0$, P passes through O, moving towards A, with speed $u \, \mathrm{m \, s^{-1}}$. The next time P passes through O is when $t = 2.5$ s.

    a Find the value of u.

    b Find the speed of P when $t = 3$ s.

    c Find the distance of P from A when $t = 3$ s.

2 A particle P of mass 1.2 kg moves along the x-axis. At time $t = 0$, P passes through the origin O, moving in the positive x-direction. At time t seconds, the velocity of P is $v \, \mathrm{m \, s^{-1}}$ and $OP = x$ metres. The resultant force acting on P has magnitude $6(2.5 - x)$ N and acts in the positive x-direction. The maximum speed of P is $8 \, \mathrm{m \, s^{-1}}$.

    a Write down the value of x when the speed of P is $8 \, \mathrm{m \, s^{-1}}$.

    b Find an expression for v^2 in terms of x.

3 A particle P of mass $0.6\,\text{kg}$ moves along the positive x-axis under the action of a single force which is directed towards the origin O and has magnitude $\dfrac{k}{(x+2)^2}\,\text{N}$ where $OP = x$ metres and k is a constant. Initially P is moving away from O. At $x = 2$ the speed of P is $8\,\text{m s}^{-1}$ and at $x = 10$ the speed of P is $2\,\text{m s}^{-1}$.

a Find the value of k.

The particle first comes to instantaneous rest at the point B.

b Find the distance OB.

4 A particle P moves along the x-axis in such a way that at time t seconds its distance x metres from the origin O is given by $x = 3\sin\left(\dfrac{\pi t}{4}\right)$.

a Prove that P moves with simple harmonic motion.

b Write down the amplitude and the period of the motion.

c Find the maximum speed of P.

The points A and B are on the same side of O with $OA = 1.2\,\text{m}$ and $OB = 2\,\text{m}$.

d Find the time taken by P to travel directly from A to B.

5 A particle P of mass $0.5\,\text{kg}$ is attached to one end of a light elastic string of natural length $1.2\,\text{m}$ and modulus of elasticity $\lambda\,\text{N}$. The other end of the string is attached to a fixed point A. The particle is hanging in equilibrium at the point O, which is $1.4\,\text{m}$ vertically below A.

a Find the value of λ.

The particle is now displaced to a point B, $1.75\,\text{m}$ vertically below A, and released from rest.

b Prove that while the string is taut P moves with simple harmonic motion.

c Find the period of the simple harmonic motion.

d Calculate the speed of P at the first instant when the string becomes slack.

e Find the greatest height reached by P above O.

6 A spacecraft S of mass m is moving in a straight line towards the centre of the Earth. When the distance of S from the centre of the Earth is x metres, the force exerted by the Earth on S has magnitude $\dfrac{k}{x^2}$, where k is a constant, and is directed towards the centre of the Earth.

a By modelling the Earth as a sphere of radius R and S as a particle, show that $k = mgR^2$.

The spacecraft starts from rest when $x = 5R$.

b Assuming that air resistance can be ignored find the speed of S as it crashes onto the Earth's surface.

7 A particle P of mass m is attached to the mid-point of a light elastic string of natural length $4l$ and modulus of elasticity $5mg$. One end of the string is attached to a fixed point A and the other end to a fixed point B, where A and B lie on a smooth horizontal surface and $AB = 6l$. The particle is held at the point C where A, C and B are collinear and $AC = \dfrac{9l}{4}$, and released from rest.

a Prove that P moves with simple harmonic motion.

Find, in terms of g and l,

b the period of the motion,

c the maximum speed of P.

8 A particle P of mass 0.5 kg is moving along the x-axis, in the positive x-direction. At time t seconds (where $t > 0$) the resultant force acting on P has magnitude $\dfrac{5}{\sqrt{(3t + 4)}}$ N and is directed towards the origin O. When $t = 0$, P is moving through O with speed $12\,\mathrm{m\,s^{-1}}$.

a Find an expression for the velocity of P at time t seconds.

b Find the distance of P from O when P is instantaneously at rest.

9 A particle P of mass 0.6 kg is attached to one end of a light elastic spring of natural length 2.5 m and modulus of elasticity 25 N. The other end of the spring is attached to a fixed point A on the smooth horizontal table on which P lies. The particle is held at the point B where $AB = 4$ m and released from rest.

a Prove that P moves with simple harmonic motion.

b Find the period and amplitude of the motion.

c Find the time taken for P to move 2 m from B.

10 A particle P of mass 0.4 kg is attached to the mid-point of a light elastic string of natural length 1.2 m and modulus of elasticity 2.5 N. The ends of the string are attached to points A and B on a smooth horizontal table where $AB = 2$ m. The particle P is released from rest at the point C on the table, where A, C and B lie in a straight line and $AC = 0.7$ m.

a Show that P moves with simple harmonic motion.

b Find the period of the motion.

The point D lies between A and B and $AD = 0.85$ m.

c Find the time taken by P to reach D for the first time.

Summary of key points

1 For a particle of mass m moving in a straight line under the influence of a force $F = \mathrm{F}(t)$

$$m\frac{\mathrm{d}v}{\mathrm{d}t} = \mathrm{F}(t)$$

2 For a particle of mass m moving in a straight line under the influence of a force $F = \mathrm{G}(x)$

$$m\frac{\mathrm{d}}{\mathrm{d}x}\left(\frac{1}{2}v^2\right) = mv\frac{\mathrm{d}v}{\mathrm{d}x} = \mathrm{G}(x)$$

3 The impulse of a variable force $\mathrm{F}(t)$ acting over the time interval t_1 to t_2 is

$$\int_{t_1}^{t_2} \mathrm{F}(t)\,\mathrm{d}t$$

4 The work done by a variable force $\mathrm{G}(x)$ which moves its point of application from x_1 to x_2 is

$$\int_{x_1}^{x_2} \mathrm{G}(x)\,\mathrm{d}x$$

5 The universal law of gravitation

The force of attraction between two bodies is directly proportional to the product of their masses and inversely proportional to the square of the distance between them.

$$F \propto \frac{M_1 M_2}{d^2}$$

where M_1 and M_2 are the masses of the two bodies and d is the distance between them.

This law is also known as Newton's law of gravitation. This force of attraction must be used when considering the motion of objects moving in space.

6   A particle which moves on a straight line so that its acceleration is always directed towards a fixed point O of the line and is proportional to its displacement from O is said to be moving with simple harmonic motion (S.H.M.).

The equation of motion can be written $\ddot{x} = -\omega^2 x$

The maximum displacement of the particle from O is the amplitude, a, of the motion.

The period of the motion is $\frac{2\pi}{\omega}$

The speed, v, at any point is given by $v^2 = \omega^2(a^2 - x^2)$

and $x = a \sin \omega t$ if $x = 0$ when $t = 0$
$x = a \cos \omega t$ if $x = a$ when $t = 0$
$x = a \sin(\omega t + \alpha)$ if x has some other value when $t = 0$

7   For a particle moving on a smooth horizontal surface attached to one end of an elastic spring
* the particle will move with S.H.M.
* the particle will perform complete oscillations.

For a particle moving on a smooth horizontal surface attached to one end of an elastic string
* the particle will move with S.H.M. while the string is taut
* the particle will move with constant speed while the string is slack.

8   For a particle hanging in equilibrium attached to one end of an elastic spring and displaced vertically from its equilibrium position
* the particle will move with S.H.M.
* the particle will perform complete oscillations
* the centre of oscillation will be the equilibrium position.

For a particle hanging in equilibrium attached to one end of an elastic string and displaced vertically from its equilibrium position
* the particle will move with S.H.M. while the string is taut
* the particle will perform complete oscillations if the amplitude is no greater than the equilibrium extension
* if the amplitude is greater than the equilibrium extension the particle will move freely under gravity while the string is slack.

Review Exercise

1 A particle P moves in a straight line. At time t seconds, the acceleration of P is e^{2t} m s^{-2}, where $t \geq 0$. When $t = 0$, P is at rest. Show that the speed, v m s^{-1}, of P at time t seconds is given by

$$v = \tfrac{1}{2}(e^{2t} - 1)$$ **E**

2 A particle P moves along the x-axis in such a way that when its displacement from the origin O is x m, its velocity is v m s^{-1} and its acceleration is $4x$ m s^{-2}. When $x = 2$, $v = 4$.

Show that $v^2 = 4x^2$. **E**

3 A particle P moves along the x-axis in the positive direction. At time t seconds, the velocity of P is v m s^{-1} and its acceleration is $\tfrac{1}{2}e^{-\frac{1}{6}t}$ m s^{-2}. When $t = 0$ the speed of P is 10 m s^{-1}.

a Express v in terms of t.

b Find, to 3 significant figures, the speed of P when $t = 3$.

c Find the limiting value of v. **E**

4 A particle P moves on the positive x-axis. When $OP = x$ metres, where O is the origin, the acceleration of P is directed away from O and has magnitude

$\left(1 - \dfrac{4}{x^2}\right)$ m s^{-2}. When $OP = x$ metres,

the velocity of P is v m s^{-1}. Given that when $x = 1$, $v = 3\sqrt{2}$ show that when

$x = \tfrac{3}{2}$, $v^2 = \dfrac{49}{3}$. **E**

5 A particle P is moving in a straight line. When P is at a distance x metres from a fixed point O on the line, the acceleration of P is $(5 + 3\sin 3x)$ m s^{-2} in the direction OP. Given that P passes through O with speed 4 m s^{-1}, find the speed of P at $x = 6$. Give your answer to 3 significant figures.

6 A particle P is moving along the positive x-axis in the direction of x increasing. When $OP = x$ metres, the velocity of P is v m s^{-1}

and the acceleration of P is $\dfrac{4k^2}{(x + 1)^2}$ m s^{-2},

where k is a positive constant. At $x = 1$, $v = 0$.

a Find v^2 in terms of x and k.

b Deduce that v cannot exceed $2k$.

7 A particle P moves along the x-axis. At time $t = 0$, P passes through the origin O, moving in the positive x-direction. At time t seconds, the velocity of P is $v\,\mathrm{m\,s^{-1}}$ and $OP = x$ metres. The acceleration of P is $\frac{1}{12}(30 - x)\,\mathrm{m\,s^{-2}}$, measured in the positive x-direction.

a Give a reason why the maximum speed of P occurs when $x = 30$.

Given that the maximum speed of P is $10\,\mathrm{m\,s^{-1}}$,

b find an expression for v^2 in terms of x. **(E)**

8 A particle P moves along the x-axis. At time t seconds the velocity of P is $v\,\mathrm{m\,s^{-1}}$ and its acceleration is $2\sin\frac{1}{2}t\,\mathrm{m\,s^{-2}}$, both measured in the direction Ox. Given that $v = 4$ when $t = 0$,

a find v in terms of t,

b calculate the distance travelled by P between the times $t = 0$ and $t = \frac{\pi}{2}$. **(E)**

9 A particle P moves along the x-axis. At time t seconds its acceleration is $(-4e^{-2t})\,\mathrm{m\,s^{-2}}$ in the direction of x increasing. When $t = 0$, P is at the origin O and is moving with speed $1\,\mathrm{m\,s^{-1}}$ in the direction of x increasing.

a Find an expression for the velocity of P at time t.

b Find the distance of P from O when P comes to instantaneous rest. **(E)**

10 At time $t = 0$, a particle P is at the origin O moving with speed $18\,\mathrm{m\,s^{-1}}$ along the x-axis in the positive x-direction. At time t seconds ($t > 0$) the acceleration of P has magnitude $\dfrac{3}{\sqrt{(t + 4)}}\,\mathrm{m\,s^{-2}}$ and is directed towards O.

a Show that, at time t seconds, the velocity of P is $[30 - 6\sqrt{(t + 4)}]\,\mathrm{m\,s^{-1}}$.

b Find the distance of P from O when P comes to instantaneous rest. **(E)**

11 A particle P starts at rest and moves in a straight line. The acceleration of P initially has magnitude $20\,\mathrm{m\,s^{-2}}$ and, in a first model of the motion of P, it is assumed that this acceleration remains constant.

a For this model, find the distance moved by P while accelerating from rest to a speed of $6\,\mathrm{m\,s^{-1}}$.

The acceleration of P when it is x metres from its initial position is $a\,\mathrm{m\,s^{-2}}$ and it is then established that $a = 12$ when $x = 2$. A refined model is proposed in which $a = p - qx$, where p and q are constants.

b Show that, under the refined model, $p = 20$ and $q = 4$.

c Hence find, for this model, the distance moved by P in first attaining a speed of $6\,\mathrm{m\,s^{-1}}$. **(E)**

12 A particle moving in a straight line starts from rest at a point O at time $t = 0$. At time t seconds, the velocity $v\,\mathrm{m\,s^{-1}}$ is given by

$$v = \begin{cases} 3t(t - 4), & 0 \leqslant t \leqslant 5 \\ 75t^{-1}, & 5 < t \leqslant 10 \end{cases}$$

a Sketch a velocity–time graph for the particle for $0 \leqslant t \leqslant 10$.

b Find the set of values of t for which the acceleration of the particle is positive.

c Show that the total distance travelled by the particle in the interval $0 \leqslant t \leqslant 5$ is $39\,\mathrm{m}$.

d Find, to 3 significant figures, the value of t at which the particle returns to O. **(E)**

13 A particle P moves along the positive x-axis. When $OP = x$ metres, the velocity of P is $v\,\mathrm{m\,s^{-1}}$ and its acceleration is $\dfrac{72}{(2x + 1)^2}\,\mathrm{m\,s^{-2}}$ in the direction of x increasing. Initially $x = 1$ and P is moving toward O with speed $6\,\mathrm{m\,s^{-1}}$. Find

a v in terms of x,

b the minimum distance of P from O.

14 A particle moves on the positive x-axis. The particle is moving towards the origin O when it passes through the point A, where $x = 2a$, with speed $\sqrt{\left(\frac{k}{a}\right)}$, where k is a constant. Given that the particle experiences an acceleration $\frac{k}{2x^2} + \frac{k}{4a^2}$ in a direction away from O,

a show that it comes instantaneously to rest at a point B, where $x = a$.

As soon as the particle reaches B the acceleration changes to $\frac{k}{2x^2} - \frac{k}{4a^2}$ in a direction away from O.

b Show that the particle next comes instantaneously to rest at A. **E**

15 A car is travelling along a straight horizontal road. As it passes a point O on the road, the engine is switched off. At time t seconds after the car has passed O, it is at a point P, where $OP = x$ metres, and its velocity is $v\,\mathrm{m\,s^{-1}}$. The motion of the car is modelled by

$$v = \frac{1}{p + qt}$$

where p and q are positive constants.

a Show that, with this model, the retardation of the car is proportional to the square of the speed.

When $t = 0$, the retardation of the car is $0.75\,\mathrm{m\,s^{-2}}$ and $v = 20$. Using the model, find

b the value of p and the value of q,

c x in terms of t.

16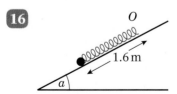

A particle of mass 0.8 kg is attached to one end of a light elastic spring, of natural length 2 m and modulus of elasticity 20 N.

The other end of the spring is attached to a fixed point O on a smooth plane which is inclined at an angle α to the horizontal, where $\tan \alpha = \frac{3}{4}$.

The particle is held at a point which is 1.6 m down the line of greatest slope of the plane from O, as shown in the figure. The particle is then released from rest.

Find the initial acceleration of the particle. **E**

17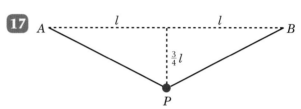

The figure shows a particle P, of mass $6M$, suspended by two light elastic strings from points A and B which are fixed and at a horizontal distance $2l$ apart. Each string has natural length l and P rests in equilibrium at a vertical distance $\frac{3}{4}l$ below the level of AB. Determine

a the tension in either string,

b the modulus of elasticity of either string. **E**

18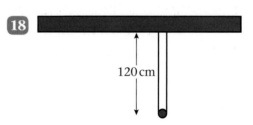

A particle of mass 5 kg is attached to one end of two light elastic strings. The other ends of the string are attached to a hook on a beam. The particle hangs in equilibrium at a distance 120 cm below the hook with both strings vertical, as shown in the figure. One string has natural length 100 cm and modulus of elasticity 175 N. The other string has natural length 90 cm and modulus of elasticity λ newtons.

Find the value of λ. **E**

19

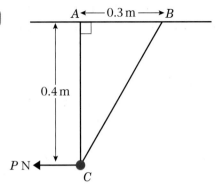

The figure shows a particle C of mass 2 kg suspended by two strings. The strings are fixed to two points A and B on a horizontal ceiling, where $AB = 0.3$ m. The string AC is light and inextensible, with length 0.4 m, while the string BC is light and elastic with natural length 0.4 m and modulus of elasticity 32 N. A horizontal force of magnitude P N holds the system in equilibrium with AC vertical.

a Show that the tension in BC is 8 N.

b Find the value of P.

c Find the tension in AC. **E**

21

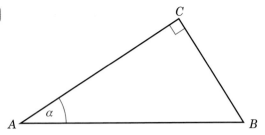

A rod AB, of mass $2m$ and length $2a$, is suspended from a fixed point C by two light strings AC and BC. The rod rests horizontally in equilibrium with AC making an angle α with the rod, where $\tan \alpha = \frac{3}{4}$, and with AC perpendicular to BC, as shown in the figure.

a Give a reason why the rod cannot be uniform.

b Show that the tension in BC is $\frac{8}{5}mg$ and find the tension in AC.

The string BC is elastic, with natural length a and modulus of elasticity kmg, where k is a constant.

c Find the value of k. **E**

20

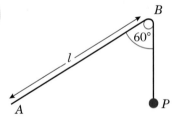

A light elastic string, of natural length l and modulus of elasticity $4mg$, has one end tied to a fixed point A. The string passes over a fixed small smooth peg B and at the other end a particle P, of mass m, is attached. The particle hangs in equilibrium. The distance between A and B is l and AB is inclined at 60° to the vertical, as shown in the figure.

a Find, in terms of l, the length of the vertical portion BP of the string.

b Show that the magnitude of the force exerted by the string on the peg is $mg\sqrt{3}$. **E**

22

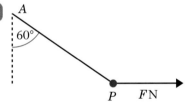

A particle of mass 0.8 kg is attached to one end of a light elastic string, of natural length 1.2 m and modulus of elasticity 24 N. The other end of the string is attached to a fixed point A. A horizontal force of magnitude F newtons is applied to P. The particle is in equilibrium with the string making an angle 60° with the downward vertical as shown in the figure. Calculate

a the value of F,

b the extension of the string,

c the elastic energy stored in the string. **E**

23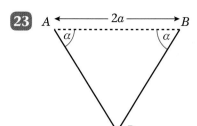

Two light elastic strings each have natural length a and modulus of elasticity λ. A particle P of mass m is attached to one end of each string. The other ends of the string are attached to points A and B, where AB is horizontal and $AB = 2a$. The particle is held at the mid-point of AB and released from rest. It comes to rest for the first time in its subsequent motion when PA and PB make angles α with AB, where $\tan \alpha = \frac{4}{3}$, as shown in the figure. Find λ in terms of m and g. **E**

24 A particle P of mass m is attached to one end of a light elastic string, of natural length a and modulus of elasticity $3.6mg$. The other end of the string is fixed at a point O on a rough horizontal table. The particle is projected along the surface of the table from O with speed $\sqrt{(2ag)}$. At its furthest point from O, the particle is at the point A, where $OA = \frac{4}{3}a$.

a Find, in terms of m, g and a, the elastic energy stored in the string when P is at A.

b Using the work–energy principle, or otherwise, find the coefficient of friction between P and the table. **E**

25 A particle P of mass m is held at a point A on a rough horizontal plane. The coefficient of friction between P and the plane is $\frac{2}{3}$. The particle is attached to one end of a light elastic string, of natural length a and modulus of elasticity $4mg$. The other end of the string is attached to a fixed point O on the plane, where $OA = \frac{3}{2}a$. The particle P is released from rest and comes to rest at a point B, where $OB < a$.

Using the work–energy principle, or otherwise, calculate the distance AB. **E**

26 One end of an light elastic string, of natural length 2 m and modulus of elasticity 19.6 N, is attached to a fixed point A. A small ball B of mass 0.5 kg is attached to the other end of the string. The ball is released from rest at A and first comes to instantaneous rest at the point C, vertically below A.

a Find the distance AC.

b Find the instantaneous acceleration of B at C. **E**

27 A light elastic string AB of natural length 1.5 m has modulus of elasticity 20 N. The end A is fixed to a point on a smooth horizontal table. A small ball S of mass 0.2 kg is attached to the end B. Initially S is at rest on the table with $AB = 1.5$ m. The ball S is then projected horizontally directly away from A with a speed of 5 m s^{-1}. By modelling S as a particle,

a find the speed of S when $AS = 2$ m.

When the speed of S is 1.5 m s^{-1}, the string breaks.

b Find the tension in the string immediately before the string breaks. **E**

28 One end of a light elastic string of natural length a and modulus of elasticity $3mg$, is fixed at a point A and the other end carries a particle P of mass m. The particle is held at A and then projected vertically downwards with speed $\sqrt{(3ga)}$.

a Find the distance AP when the acceleration of the particle is instantaneously zero.

b Find the maximum speed attained by the particle during its motion. **E**

29 A light elastic string of natural length 30 cm is placed on a smooth horizontal table with one end attached to a fixed point P on the table. The other end of the string is attached to a fixed point Q on the table such that $PQ = 80$ cm.

a Given that the tension in the string is 175 N, find, in newtons, the modulus of elasticity of the string.

The mid-point of the string is pulled a distance 30 cm along the perpendicular bisector of PQ in the plane of the table.

b Find the increase of tension in the string.

c Find, in joules, the corresponding increase in the elastic energy of the string. **E**

30 A particle P of mass m is attached to one end of a light elastic string of length a and modulus of elasticity $\frac{1}{2}mg$. The other end of the string is fixed at a point A which is at a height $2a$ above a smooth horizontal table. The particle is held on the table with the string making an angle β with the table, where $\tan \beta = \frac{3}{4}$.

a Find the elastic energy stored in the string.

The particle is now released from rest. Assuming that P remains on the table,

b find the speed of P when the string is vertical.

By finding the vertical component of the tension in the string when P is on the table and AP makes an angle θ with the horizontal,

c show that the assumption that P remains in contact with the table is justified. **E**

31 A light elastic string has natural length 4 m and modulus of elasticity 58.8 N. A particle P of mass 0.5 kg is attached to one end of the string. The other end of the

string is attached to a fixed point A. The particle is released from rest at A and falls vertically.

a Find the distance travelled by P before it comes to instantaneous rest for the first time.

The particle is now held at a point 7 m vertically below A and released from rest.

b Find the speed of the particle when the string first becomes slack. **E**

32 Two light elastic strings each have natural length 0.75 m and modulus of elasticity 49 N. A particle P of mass 2 kg is attached to one end of each string. The other ends of the strings are attached to fixed points A and B, where AB is horizontal and $AB = 1.5$ m.

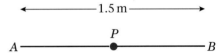

The particle is held at the mid-point of AB. The particle is released from rest, as shown in the figure.

a Find the speed of P when it has fallen a distance of 1 m.

Given instead that P hangs in equilibrium vertically below the mid-point of AB with $\angle APB = 2\alpha$,

b show that $\tan \alpha + 5 \sin \alpha = 5$. **E**

33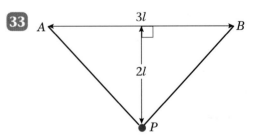

A light elastic string, of natural length $3l$ and modulus of elasticity λ, has ends attached to two points A and B where $AB = 3l$ and AB is horizontal. A particle P of mass m is attached to the mid-point of the string. Given that P rests in equilibrium at a distance $2l$ below AB, as shown in the figure,

a show that $\lambda = \dfrac{15mg}{16}$.

The particle is pulled vertically downwards from its equilibrium position until the total length of the elastic string is $7.8l$. The particle is released from rest.

b Show that P comes to instantaneous rest on the line AB.   (E)

34 A particle P, of mass m, is attached to one end of a light elastic string, of natural length l and modulus of elasticity $8mg$. The other end of the string is attached at a point A to a horizontal ceiling which is at a height $2l$ above a horizontal floor. The particle P is held at A and projected vertically downwards with speed u.

a Find the least possible value of u for P to reach the floor.

Given that $u^2 = 16gl$ and that when P strikes the floor its speed is halved, find

b the speed of P when it hits the ceiling after striking the floor once,

c the maximum speed of P during its motion.   (E)

35 A particle P of mass $0.2\,\text{kg}$ moves away from the origin along the positive x-axis. It moves under the action of a force directed away from the origin O of magnitude $\dfrac{5}{x+1}\,\text{N}$, where $OP = x\,\text{m}$. Given that the speed of P is $5\,\text{m\,s}^{-1}$ when $x = 0$, find the value of x, to 3 significant figures, when the speed of P is $15\,\text{m\,s}^{-1}$.   (E)

36 A particle P of mass $2.5\,\text{kg}$ moves along the positive x-axis. It moves away from a fixed origin O, under the action of a force directed away from O. When $OP = x$ metres, the magnitude of the force is $2e^{-0.1x}\,\text{N}$ and the speed of P is $v\,\text{m\,s}^{-1}$. When $x = 0$, $v = 2$. Find

a v^2 in terms of x,

b the value of x when $v = 4$.

c Give a reason why the speed of P does not exceed $\sqrt{20}\,\text{m\,s}^{-1}$.

37 A toy car of mass $0.2\,\text{kg}$ is travelling in a straight line on a horizontal floor. The car is modelled as a particle. At time $t = 0$ the car passes through a fixed point O. After t seconds the speed of the car is $v\,\text{m\,s}^{-1}$ and the car is at a point P with $OP = x$ metres. The resultant force on the car is modelled as $\frac{1}{10}x(4 - 3x)\,\text{N}$ in the direction OP. The car comes to instantaneous rest when $x = 6$. Find

a an expression for v^2 in terms of x,

b the initial speed of the car.   (E)

38 A particle P of mass $0.6\,\text{kg}$ is moving along the positive x-axis under the action of a force which is directed away from the origin O. At time t seconds, the force has magnitude $3e^{-0.5t}\,\text{N}$. When $t = 0$, the particle P is at O and moving with speed $2\,\text{m\,s}^{-1}$ in the direction of x increasing. Find

a the value of t when the speed is $8\,\text{m\,s}^{-1}$,

b the distance of P from O when $t = 2$.

39 A particle P of mass $m\,\text{kg}$ slides from rest down a smooth plane inclined at $30°$ to the horizontal. When P has moved a distance x metres down the plane, the resistance to motion from non-gravitational forces has magnitude $mx^2\,\text{N}$. Find

a the speed of P when $x = 2$,

b the distance P has moved when it comes to rest for the first time.   (E)

40 Above the Earth's surface, the magnitude of the force on a particle due to the Earth's gravity is inversely proportional to the square of the distance of the particle from the centre of the Earth. Assuming that the Earth is a sphere of radius R, and taking g as the acceleration due to gravity at the surface of the Earth,

a prove that the magnitude of the gravitational force on a particle of mass m when it is a distance x (where $x \geqslant R$) from the centre of the Earth is $\dfrac{mgR^2}{x^2}$.

A particle is fired vertically upwards from the surface of the Earth with initial speed u, where $u^2 = \frac{3}{2}gR$. Ignoring air resistance,

b find, in terms of g and R, the speed of the particle when it is at a height $2R$ above the surface of the Earth. **(E)**

41 A rocket is fired vertically upwards with speed U from a point on the Earth's surface. The rocket is modelled as a particle P of constant mass m, and the Earth as a fixed sphere of radius R. At a distance x from the centre of the Earth, the speed of P is v. The only force acting on P is directed towards the centre of the Earth and has magnitude $\dfrac{cm}{x^2}$, where c is a constant.

a Show that $v^2 = U^2 + 2c\left(\dfrac{1}{x} - \dfrac{1}{R}\right)$.

The kinetic energy of P at $x = 2R$ is half of the kinetic energy at $x = R$.

b Find c in terms of U and R. **(E)**

42 A projectile P is fired vertically upwards from a point on the Earth's surface. When P is at a distance x from the centre of the Earth its speed is v. Its acceleration is directed towards the centre of the Earth and has magnitude $\dfrac{k}{x^2}$, where k is a constant. The Earth is assumed to be a sphere of radius R.

a Show that the motion of P may be modelled by the differential equation

$$v\frac{dv}{dx} = -\frac{gR^2}{x^2}$$

The initial speed of P is U, where $U^2 < 2gR$. The greatest distance of P from the centre of the Earth is X.

b Find X in terms of U, R and g. **(E)**

43 A car of mass 800 kg moves along a horizontal straight road. At time t seconds, the resultant force on the car has magnitude $\dfrac{48\,000}{(t+2)^2}$ N, acting in the direction of motion of the car. When $t = 0$, the car is at rest.

a Show that the speed of the car approaches a limiting value as t increases and find this value.

b Find the distance moved by the car in the first 6 s of its motion. **(E)**

44 A particle P of mass $\frac{1}{3}$ kg moves along the positive x-axis under the action of a single force. The force is directed towards the origin O and has magnitude $\dfrac{k}{(x+1)^2}$ N, where $OP = x$ metres and k is a constant. Initially P is moving away from O. At $x = 1$ the speed of P is $4\,\text{m s}^{-1}$, and at $x = 8$ the speed of P is $\sqrt{2}\,\text{m s}^{-1}$.

a Find the value of k.

b Find the distance of P from O when P first comes to instantaneous rest. **(E)**

45 A particle P moves in a straight line with simple harmonic motion about a fixed centre O with period 2 s. At time t seconds the speed of P is $v\,\text{m s}^{-1}$. When $t = 0$, $v = 0$ and P is at a point A where $OA = 0.25$ m.

Find the smallest positive value of t for which $AP = 0.375$ m. **(E)**

46 A particle P of mass 0.2 kg oscillates with simple harmonic motion between the points A and B, coming to rest at both points. The distance AB is 0.2 m, and P completes 5 oscillations every second.

a Find, to 3 significant figures, the maximum resultant force exerted on P.

When the particle is at A, it is struck a blow in the direction BA. The particle now oscillates with simple harmonic motion with the same frequency as previously but twice the amplitude.

b Find, to 3 significant figures, the speed of the particle immediately after it has been struck. **E**

47 A piston P in a machine moves in a straight line with simple harmonic motion about a fixed centre O. The period of the oscillations is π s. When P is 0.5 m from O, its speed is 2.4 m s^{-1}. Find

a the amplitude of the motion,

b the maximum speed of P during its motion,

c the maximum magnitude of the acceleration of P during the motion,

d the total time, in seconds to 2 decimal places, in each complete oscillation for which the speed of P is greater than 2.4 m s^{-1}. **E**

48

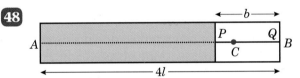

In a game at a fair, a small target C moves horizontally with simple harmonic motion between the points A and B, where $AB = 4l$. The target moves inside a box and takes 3 s to travel from A to B. A player has to shoot at C, but C is only visible to the player when it passes a window PQ where $PQ = b$. The window is initially placed with Q at the point shown in the figure above. The target takes 0.75 s to travel from Q to P.

a Show that $b = (2 - \sqrt{2})l$.

b Find the speed of C as it passes P.

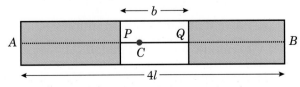

For advanced players, the window PQ is moved to the centre of AB so that $AP = QB$, as shown in the second figure above.

c Find the time, in seconds to 2 decimal places, taken for C to pass from Q to P in this new position. **E**

49 The points O, A, B and C lie in a straight line, in that order, with $OA = 0.6$ m, $OB = 0.8$ m and $OC = 1.2$ m. A particle P, moving in a straight line, has speed $\left(\frac{3}{10}\sqrt{3}\right)$ m s^{-1} at A, $\left(\frac{1}{5}\sqrt{5}\right)$ m s^{-1} at B and is instantaneously at rest at C.

a Show that this information is consistent with P performing simple harmonic motion with centre O.

Given that P is performing simple harmonic motion with centre O,

b show that the speed of P at O is 0.6 m s^{-1},

c find the magnitude of the acceleration of P as it passes A,

d find, to 3 significant figures, the time taken for P to move directly from A to B. **E**

50 The rise and fall of the water level in a harbour is modelled as simple harmonic motion. On a particular day the maximum and minimum depths of the water in the harbour are 10 m and 4 m and these occur at 1100 hours and 1700 hours respectively.

a Find the speed, in m h^{-1}, at which the water level in the harbour is falling at 1600 hours on this particular day.

b Find the total time, between 1100 hours and 2300 hours on this particular day, for which the depth in the harbour is less than 5.5 m. **E**

51 A piston in a machine is modelled as a particle of mass 0.2 kg attached to one end A of a light elastic spring, of natural length 0.6 m and modulus of elasticity 48 N. The other end B of the spring is fixed and the piston is free to move in a horizontal tube which is assumed to be smooth. The piston is released from rest when $AB = 0.9$ m.

a Prove that the motion of the piston is simple harmonic with period $\frac{\pi}{10}$ s.

b Find the maximum speed of the piston.

c Find, in terms of π, the length of time during each oscillation for which the length of the spring is less than 0.75 m. **(E)**

52 A particle P of mass 0.8 kg is attached to one end A of a light elastic spring OA, of natural length 60 cm and modulus of elasticity 12 N. The spring is placed on a smooth table and the end O is fixed. The particle is pulled away from O to a point B, where $OB = 85$ cm, and is released from rest.

a Prove that the motion of P is simple harmonic motion with period $\frac{2\pi}{5}$ s.

b Find the greatest magnitude of the acceleration of P during the motion.

Two seconds after being released from rest, P passes through the point C.

c Find, to 2 significant figures, the speed of P as it passes through C.

d State the direction in which P is moving 2 s after being released. **(E)**

53 A light elastic string of natural length l has one end attached to a fixed point A. A particle P of mass m is attached to the other end of the string and hangs in equilibrium at the point O, where $AO = \frac{5}{4}l$.

a Find the modulus of elasticity of the string.

The particle P is then pulled down and released from rest. At time t the length of the string is $\frac{5l}{4} + x$.

b Prove that, while the string is taut,

$$\frac{d^2x}{dt^2} = -\frac{4gx}{l}$$

When P is released, $AP = \frac{7}{4}l$. The point B is a distance l vertically below A.

c Find the speed of P at B.

d Describe briefly the motion of P after it has passed through B for the first time until it next passes through O. **(E)**

54 A light elastic string, of natural length $4a$ and modulus of elasticity $8mg$, has one end attached to a fixed point A. A particle P of mass m is attached to the other end of the string and hangs in equilibrium at the point O.

a Find the distance AO.

The particle is now pulled down to a point C vertically below O, where $OC = d$. It is released from rest. In the subsequent motion the string does not become slack.

b Show that P moves with simple harmonic motion of period $\pi\sqrt{\left(\frac{2a}{g}\right)}$.

The greatest speed of P during this motion is $\frac{1}{2}\sqrt{(ga)}$.

c Find d in terms of a.

Instead of being pulled down a distance d, the particle is pulled down a distance a. Without further calculation,

d describe briefly the subsequent motion of P. **(E)**

55 A particle P of mass 0.3 kg is attached to one end of a light elastic spring. The other end of the spring is attached to a fixed point O on a smooth horizontal table. The spring has natural length 2 m and modulus of elasticity 21.6 N. The particle P is placed on the table at a point A, where $OA = 2$ m. The particle P is now pulled away from O to the point B, where OAB is a straight line with $OB = 3.5$ m. It is then released from rest.

a Prove that P moves with simple harmonic motion of period $\frac{\pi}{3}$ s.

b Find the speed of P when it reaches A. The point C is the mid-point of AB.

c Find, in terms of π, the time taken for P to reach C for the first time.

Later in the motion, *P* collides with a particle *Q* of mass 0.2 kg which is at rest at *A*.

After impact, *P* and *Q* coalesce to form a single particle *R*.

d Show that *R* also moves with simple harmonic motion and find the amplitude of this motion. **E**

56

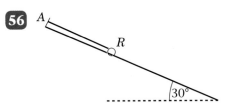

A small ring *R* of mass *m* is free to slide on a smooth straight wire which is fixed at an angle of 30° to the horizontal. The ring is attached to one end of a light elastic string of natural length *a* and modulus of elasticity λ. The other end is attached to a fixed point *A* on the wire, as shown in the figure. The ring rests in equilibrium at the point *B*, where $AB = \frac{9}{8}a$.

a Show that $\lambda = 4mg$.

The ring is pulled down to a point *C*, where $BC = \frac{1}{4}a$ and released from rest. At time *t* after *R* is released the extension in the string is $\left(\frac{1}{8}a + x\right)$.

b Obtain a differential equation for the motion of *R* while the string remains taut, and show that it represents simple harmonic motion with period $\pi\sqrt{\left(\frac{a}{g}\right)}$.

c Find, in terms of *g*, the greatest magnitude of the acceleration of *R* while the string remains taut.

d Find, in terms of *a* and *g*, the time taken for *R* to move from the point at which it first reaches a maximum speed to the point where the string becomes slack for the first time. **E**

4

After completing this chapter you should be able to:

- find the forces acting on an object moving in a horizontal or vertical circle
- determine whether an object will follow a circular path
- solve problems relating to motion in vertical or horizontal circles.

Motion in a circle

The chairs on this amusement park ride are all at the same angle to the vertical, regardless of whether or not they are occupied.

Many roads are built at a slight angle to the horizontal at roundabouts and bends. This is called **camber** and helps to reduce sideways force on a car as it turns the corner.

4.1 You can calculate the angular speed of an object moving in a circle.

When an object is moving in a straight line, the speed, usually measured in $m\,s^{-1}$ or $km\,h^{-1}$, describes the rate at which distance is changing. For an object moving on a circular path, you can use the same method for measuring speed, but it is often simpler to measure the speed by considering the rate at which the radius is turning.

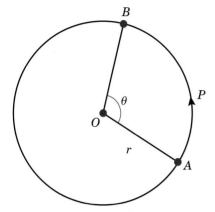

As the particle P moves from point A on the circumference of a circle of radius r m to point B, the radius of the circle turns through an angle θ radians.

The distance moved by P is $r\theta$ m, so if P is moving at $v\,m\,s^{-1}$ we know that $v = \dfrac{d}{dt}(r\theta) = r\dfrac{d\theta}{dt} = r \times \dot{\theta}$.

$\dot{\theta}$ is the rate at which the radius is turning about O.

Although it describes the motion of the radius, $\dot{\theta}$ is usually called the **angular speed of the particle** about O.

The angular speed of a particle is usually denoted by ω, and measured in $rad\,s^{-1}$.

■ **If a particle is moving around a circle of radius r m with linear speed $v\,m\,s^{-1}$ and angular speed $\omega\,rad\,s^{-1}$ then $v = r\omega$.**

Example 1

A particle moves in a circle of radius 4 m with speed $2\,m\,s^{-1}$. Calculate the angular speed.

Using $v = r\omega$, $2 = 4\omega$, so $\omega = 0.5\,rad\,s^{-1}$

Example 2

Express an angular speed of 200 revolutions per minute in radians per second.

Each complete revolution is 2π radians, so 200 revolutions is 400π radians per minute. Therefore the angular speed is $\dfrac{400\pi}{60} \approx 20.9\,rads\,s^{-1}$.

Sometimes an angular speed is described in terms of the number of revolutions completed in a given time.

Example **3**

A particle moves round a circle in 10 seconds at a constant speed of $15\,\text{m s}^{-1}$. Calculate the angular speed of the particle and the radius of the circle.

The particle rotates through an angle of 2π radians in 10 seconds, so $\omega = \dfrac{2\pi}{10} \approx 0.628\,\text{rad s}^{-1}$.

Using $v = r\omega$, $r = \dfrac{v}{\omega} = \dfrac{15}{0.628} \approx 23.9\,\text{m}$.

Exercise **4A**

1 Express

    a an angular speed of 5 revolutions per minute in rad s^{-1},

    b an angular speed of 120 revolutions per minute in rad s^{-1},

    c an angular speed of $4\,\text{rad s}^{-1}$ in revolutions per minute,

    d an angular speed of $3\,\text{rad s}^{-1}$ in revolutions per hour.

2 Find the speed in m s^{-1} of a particle moving on a circular path of radius $20\,\text{m}$ at

    a $4\,\text{rad s}^{-1}$,

    b $40\,\text{rev min}^{-1}$.

3 A particle moves on a circular path of radius $25\,\text{cm}$ at a constant speed of $2\,\text{m s}^{-1}$. Find the angular speed of the particle

    a in rad s^{-1},

    b in rev min^{-1}.

4 Find the speed in m s^{-1} of a particle moving on a circular path of radius $80\,\text{cm}$ at

    a $2.5\,\text{rad s}^{-1}$,

    b $25\,\text{rev min}^{-1}$.

5 An athlete is running round a circular track of radius $50\,\text{m}$ at $7\,\text{m s}^{-1}$.

    a How long does it take the athlete to complete one circuit of the track?

    b Find the angular speed of the athlete in rad s^{-1}.

6 A disc of radius $12\,\text{cm}$ rotates at a constant angular speed, completing one revolution every 10 seconds. Find

    a the angular speed of the disc in rad s^{-1},

    b the speed of a particle on the outer rim of the disc in m s^{-1},

    c the speed of a particle at a point $8\,\text{cm}$ from the centre of the disc in m s^{-1}.

7 A cyclist completes two circuits of a circular track in 45 seconds. Calculate
   a his angular speed in rad s^{-1},
   b the radius of the track given that his speed is 40 km h^{-1}.

8 Anish and Bethany are on a fairground roundabout. Anish is 3 m from the centre and Bethany is 5 m from the centre. If the roundabout completes 10 revolutions per minute, calculate the speeds with which Anish and Bethany are moving.

9 A model train completes one circuit of a circular track of radius 1.5 m in 26 seconds. Calculate
   a the angular speed of the train in rad s^{-1},
   b the linear speed of the train in m s^{-1}.

10 A train is moving at 150 km h^{-1} round a circular bend of radius 750 m. Calculate the angular speed of the train in rad s^{-1}.

11 The hour hand on a clock has radius 10 cm, and the minute hand has radius 15 cm. Calculate
   a the angular speed of the end of each hand,
   b the linear speed of the end of each hand.

12 The drum of a washing machine has diameter 50 cm. The drum spins at 1200 rev min^{-1}. Find the linear speed of a point on the drum.

13 A gramophone record rotates at 45 rev min^{-1}.
   a Find the angular speed of the record in rad s^{-1}.
   b Find the distance from the centre of a point moving at 12 cm s^{-1}.

14 The Earth completes one orbit of the sun in a year. Taking the orbit to be a circle of radius 1.5×10^{11} m, and a year to be 365 days, calculate the speed at which the Earth is moving.

4.2 You can calculate the acceleration of an object moving on a horizontal circular path.

When an object moves round a horizontal circular path at constant speed, the direction of the motion is changing. If the direction is changing, then, although the speed is constant, the velocity is not constant. If the velocity is changing then the object must have an acceleration.

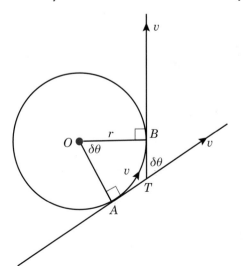

Suppose that the object is moving on a circular path of radius r at constant speed v.

Let the time taken to move from A to B be δt, and the angle AOB be $\delta\theta$.

At A, the velocity is v along the tangent AT. At B, the velocity is v along the tangent TB.

The velocity at B can be resolved into components:

    $v \cos \delta\theta$ parallel to AT and
    $v \sin \delta\theta$ perpendicular to AT.

We know that acceleration $= \dfrac{\text{change in velocity}}{\text{time}}$, so to find the acceleration of the object at the instant when it passes point A, we need to consider what happens to $\dfrac{v\cos \delta\theta - v}{\delta t}$ and $\dfrac{v\sin \delta\theta - 0}{\delta t}$ as $\delta t \to 0$ for the components of the acceleration parallel to AT and perpendicular to AT respectively.

For a small angle $\delta\theta$ measured in radians, $\cos \delta\theta \approx 1$ and $\sin \delta\theta \approx \delta\theta$, so the acceleration parallel to AT is zero, and the acceleration perpendicular to AT is $v\dfrac{\delta\theta}{\delta t} = v\omega$.

Using $v = r\omega$, $v\omega$ can be written as $r\omega^2$ or $\dfrac{v^2}{r}$.

■ Using $v = r\omega$, the acceleration of the object is $r\omega^2$, or $\dfrac{v^2}{r}$, towards the centre of the circle.

Example 4

A particle is moving on a horizontal circular path of radius 20 cm with constant angular speed $2 \, \text{rad s}^{-1}$. Calculate the acceleration of the particle.

Acceleration

$= 0.2 \times 2^2$

$= 0.8 \, \text{m s}^{-2}$ towards the centre of the circle.

Using $a = r\omega^2$.

The radius needs to be measured in metres if the answer is to be in m s^{-2}.

Example 5

A particle of mass 150 g moves in a horizontal circle of radius 50 cm at a constant speed of $4 \, \text{m s}^{-1}$. Find the force towards the centre of the circle that must act on the particle.

Force $= \dfrac{0.15 \times 4^2}{0.5} = 4.8 \, \text{N}$

Using $a = \dfrac{v^2}{r}$.

The mass needs to be in kg, and the radius in m. The speed is already in m s^{-1}.

Example 6

One end of a light inextensible string of length 20 cm is attached to a particle P of mass 250 g. The other end of the string is attached to a fixed point O on a smooth horizontal table. P moves in a horizontal circle centre O at constant angular speed $3 \, \text{rad s}^{-1}$. Find the tension in the string.

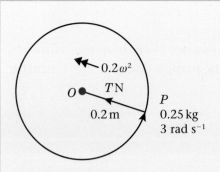

Suppose that the tension in the string is TN.

Then $T = mr\omega^2 = 0.25 \times 0.2 \times 9 = 0.45$ N.

The force towards the centre of the circle is due to the tension in the string.

Resolve towards the centre of the circle.

Example 7

A smooth wire is formed into a circle of radius 15 cm. A bead of mass 50 g is threaded onto the wire. The wire is horizontal and the bead is made to move along it with a constant speed of 20 cm s⁻¹. Find the horizontal component of the force on the bead due to the wire.

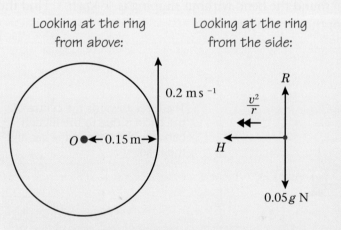

Looking at the ring from above:

Looking at the ring from the side:

Let the horizontal component of the force exerted on the bead by the ring be H.

$$H = \frac{mv^2}{r} = \frac{0.05 \times 0.2^2}{0.15} \approx 0.013 \text{ N}$$

The forces acting on the bead are weight $0.05g$ N, the normal reaction, R, and the horizontal force, H.

The force towards the centre of the circle is due to the horizontal component of the reaction between the ring and the bead.

Resolve towards the centre of the circle.

Example 8

A particle P of mass 10 g rests on a rough horizontal disc at a distance 15 cm from the centre. The disc rotates at constant angular speed of 1.2 rad s^{-1}, and the particle does not slip. Calculate the force due to the friction acting on the particle.

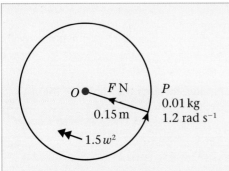

O $F \text{ N}$
0.15 m
$1.5 \, w^2$
P
0.01 kg
1.2 rad s^{-1}

The force towards the centre of the circle is due to the friction between the particle and the disc.

Suppose that the frictional force is $F \text{ N}$.

Then $F = mr\omega^2 = 0.01 \times 0.15 \times 1.2^2 = 0.00216 \text{ N}$.

Resolve towards the centre of the circle.

Example 9

A car of mass M kg is travelling round a bend which is an arc of a circle of radius 140 m. The greatest speed at which the car can travel round the bend without slipping is 45 km h^{-1}. Find the coefficient of friction between the tyres of the car and the road.

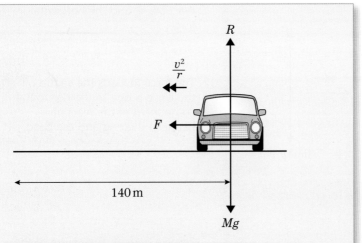

R
$\dfrac{v^2}{r}$
F
140 m
Mg

The force towards the centre of the circle is due to the friction between the tyres of the car and the road.

Mark the forces on the diagram and resolve in the direction of the acceleration and perpendicular to it, i.e. horizontally and vertically.

Let the frictional force between the car tyres and the road be F, and the coefficient of friction be μ. The normal reaction between the car and the road is R.

$R(\uparrow): R = Mg$

$R(\leftarrow): F = F_{max} = \dfrac{mv^2}{r}$

As the car is about to slip at this speed, we know that $F = F_{max} = \mu R$.

Resolve towards the centre of the circle.

$$v = 45\,\text{km}\,\text{h}^{-1} = \frac{45 \times 1000}{3600} = 12.5\,\text{m}\,\text{s}^{-1}$$

Convert the speed from $\text{km}\,\text{h}^{-1}$ to $\text{m}\,\text{s}^{-1}$ so that the units are consistent.

$$\Rightarrow \mu Mg = \frac{M \times 12.5^2}{140}$$

You do not need to know the value of M because it is a common factor on both sides of the equation.

$$\mu = \frac{12.5^2}{140 \times g} \approx 0.11$$

Exercise 4B

Whenever a numerical value of g is required take $g = 9.8\,\text{m}\,\text{s}^{-2}$.

1 A particle is moving on a horizontal circular path of radius 16 cm with a constant angular speed of $5\,\text{rad}\,\text{s}^{-1}$. Calculate the acceleration of the particle.

2 A particle is moving on a horizontal circular path of radius 0.3 m at a constant speed of $2.5\,\text{m}\,\text{s}^{-1}$. Calculate the acceleration of the particle.

3 A particle is moving on a horizontal circular path of radius 3 m. Given that the acceleration of the particle is $75\,\text{m}\,\text{s}^{-2}$ towards the centre of the circle, find

   a the angular speed of the particle,

   b the linear speed of the particle.

4 A particle is moving on a horizontal circular path of diameter 1.2 m. Given that the acceleration of the particle is $100\,\text{m}\,\text{s}^{-2}$ towards the centre of the circle, find

   a the angular speed of the particle,

   b the linear speed of the particle.

5 A car is travelling round a bend which is an arc of a circle of radius 90 m. The speed of the car is $50\,\text{km}\,\text{h}^{-1}$. Calculate its acceleration.

6 A car moving along a horizontal road which follows an arc of a circle of radius 75 m has an acceleration of $6\,\text{m}\,\text{s}^{-2}$ directed towards the centre of the circle. Calculate the angular speed of the car.

7 One end of a light inextensible string of length 0.15 m is attached to a particle P of mass 300 g. The other end of the string is attached to a fixed point O on a smooth horizontal table. P moves in a horizontal circle centre O at constant angular speed $4\,\text{rad}\,\text{s}^{-1}$. Find the tension in the string.

8 One end of a light inextensible string of length 25 cm is attached to a particle P of mass 150 g. The other end of the string is attached to a fixed point O on a smooth horizontal table. P moves in a horizontal circle centre O at constant speed $9\,\text{m}\,\text{s}^{-1}$. Find the tension in the string.

9 A smooth wire is formed into a circle of radius 0.12 m. A bead of mass 60 g is threaded onto the wire. The wire is horizontal and the bead is made to move along it with a constant speed of 3 m s^{-1}. Find

  a the vertical component of the force on the bead due to the wire,

  b the horizontal component of the force on the bead due to the wire.

10 A particle P of mass 15 g rests on a rough horizontal disc at a distance 12 cm from the centre. The disc rotates at a constant angular speed of 2 rad s^{-1}, and the particle does not slip. Calculate

  a the linear speed of the particle,

  b the force due to the friction acting on the particle.

11 A particle P rests on a rough horizontal disc at a distance 20 cm from the centre. When the disc rotates at constant angular speed of 1.2 rad s^{-1}, the particle is just about to slip. Calculate the value of the coefficient of friction between the particle and the disc.

12 A particle P of mass 0.3 kg rests on a rough horizontal disc at a distance 0.25 m from the centre of the disc. The coefficient of friction between the particle and the disc is 0.25. Given that P is on the point of slipping, find the angular speed of the disc.

13 A car is travelling round a bend in the road which is an arc of a circle of radius 80 m. The greatest speed at which the car can travel round the bend without slipping is 40 km h^{-1}. Find the coefficient of friction between the tyres of the car and the road.

14 A car is travelling round a bend in the road which is an arc of a circle of radius 60 m. The coefficient of friction between the tyres of the car and the road is $\frac{1}{3}$. Find the greatest angular speed at which the car can travel round the bend without slipping.

15 One end of a light extensible string of natural length 0.3 m and modulus of elasticity 10 N is attached to a particle P of mass 250 g. The other end of the string is attached to a fixed point O on a smooth horizontal table. P moves in a horizontal circle centre O at constant angular speed 3 rad s^{-1}. Find the radius of the circle.

16 A centrifuge consists of a vertical hollow cylinder of radius 20 cm rotating about a vertical axis through its centre at 90 rev s^{-1}. Calculate the magnitude of the normal reaction between the cylinder and a particle of mass 5 g on the inner surface of the cylinder.

17 A fairground ride consists of a vertical hollow cylinder of diameter 5 m which rotates about a vertical axis through its centre. When the ride is rotating at W rad s^{-1} the floor of the cylinder opens. The people on the ride remain, without slipping, in contact with the inner surface of the cylinder. Given that the coefficient of friction between a person and the inner surface of the cylinder is $\frac{2}{3}$, find the minimum value for W.

18 Two particles P and Q, both of mass 80 g, are attached to the ends of a light inextensible string of length 30 cm. Particle P is on a smooth horizontal table, the string passes through a small smooth hole in the centre of the table, and particle Q hangs freely below the table at the other end of the string. P is moving on a circular path about the centre of the table at constant linear speed. Find the linear speed at which P must move if Q is in equilibrium 10 cm below the table.

4.3 **You can solve three-dimensional problems about objects moving in horizontal circles.**

In this section you will find out how the method of resolving forces can be used to solve a problem about an object moving in a horizontal circle.

Example 10

A particle of mass 2 kg is attached to one end of a light inextensible string of length 50 cm. The other end of the string is attached to a fixed point A. The particle moves with constant angular speed in a horizontal circle of radius 40 cm. The centre of the circle is vertically below A. Calculate the tension in the string and the angular speed of the particle.

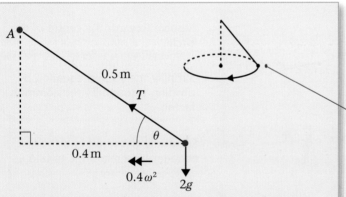

Summarise the information in a diagram.

As the particle moves round the circle, the string follows the surface of a cone – this model is called a **conical pendulum.**

Let the tension in the string be T, and the angular speed be ω.

Suppose that the string is inclined at angle θ to the horizontal.

Name any dimensions and forces that you might want to use or find in your working.

Then R($\uparrow$): $T\sin\theta = 2g$

and R($\leftarrow$): $T\cos\theta = 2 \times 0.4 \times \omega^2$

But from the dimensions given we know that
$\cos\theta = \frac{4}{5}$ and $\sin\theta = \frac{3}{5}$

so, $T = 2g \times \frac{5}{3} \approx 32.7\,\text{N}$

and $\omega^2 = \dfrac{T\cos\theta}{0.8} = \dfrac{32.7 \times 0.8}{0.8} = 32.7$

$\omega \approx 5.7\,\text{rad s}^{-1}$.

Resolve T into horizontal and vertical components.

Resolve towards the centre of the circle.

The diagram is a 3, 4, 5 triangle.

Substitute the values of $\cos\theta$ and $\sin\theta$ to solve the equations.

Example 11

A particle of mass m is attached to one end of a light inextensible string of length l. The other end of the string is attached to a fixed point A. The particle moves with constant angular speed in a horizontal circle. The string is taut and the angle between the string and the vertical is θ. The centre of the circle is vertically below A. Find the angular speed of the particle.

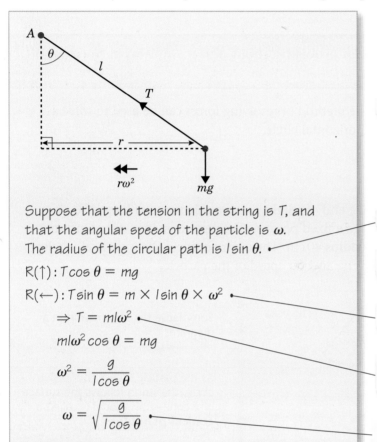

Suppose that the tension in the string is T, and that the angular speed of the particle is ω. The radius of the circular path is $l\sin\theta$.

$R(\uparrow): T\cos\theta = mg$

$R(\leftarrow): T\sin\theta = m \times l\sin\theta \times \omega^2$

$\Rightarrow T = ml\omega^2$

$ml\omega^2 \cos\theta = mg$

$\omega^2 = \dfrac{g}{l\cos\theta}$

$\omega = \sqrt{\dfrac{g}{l\cos\theta}}$

Draw and label a diagram.

Use the right-angled triangle.

Resolve T into horizontal and vertical components.

Resolve towards the centre of the circle.

Simplify the second equation by dividing through by the common factor.

Substitute the result into the first equation and rearrange to find ω.

Example 12

A car travels round a bend of radius $500\,\text{m}$ on a road which is banked at an angle θ to the horizontal. The car is assumed to be moving at constant speed in a horizontal circle. If there is no frictional force acting on the car when it is travelling at $90\,\text{km h}^{-1}$, find the value of θ.

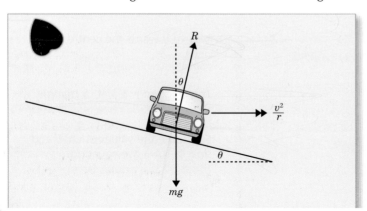

Draw and label a diagram.

Suppose that the mass of the car is m, and that the normal reaction is R.

$$90 \,\text{km h}^{-1} = \frac{90 \times 1000}{3600} = 25 \,\text{m s}^{-1}$$

$$R(\uparrow): R\cos\theta = mg$$

Resolve the normal reaction into vertical and horizontal components.

$$R(\leftarrow): R\sin\theta = \frac{m \times 25^2}{500}$$

Resolve towards the centre of the circle.

$$\Rightarrow \tan\theta = \frac{25^2}{500 \times g} \approx 0.128, \ \theta \approx 7.3°$$

Divide the second equation by the first.

Example 13

The diagram shows a particle P of mass m attached by two strings to fixed points A and B, where A is vertically above B. The strings are both taut and P is moving in a horizontal circle with constant angular speed $2\sqrt{3g}$ rad s^{-1}.

Both strings are 0.5 m in length and inclined at 60° to the vertical.

Calculate the tensions in the two strings.

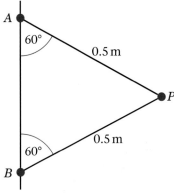

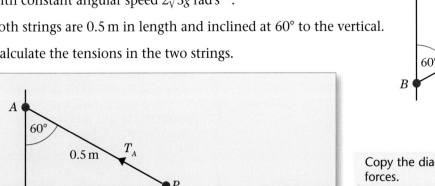

Copy the diagram and show all the forces.

The radius of the circular path is

$$0.5\cos 30° = \frac{\sqrt{3}}{4}\,\text{m}$$

This is an equilateral triangle.

$$R(\uparrow): T_A\cos 60 = T_B\cos 60 + mg$$

$$\therefore T_A - T_B = 2mg \qquad \text{①}$$

Resolve both tensions into their horizontal and vertical components.

$$R(\leftarrow): T_A\cos 30 + T_B\cos 30 = mr\omega^2$$

Resolve towards the centre of the circle.

$$\therefore \frac{\sqrt{3}}{2}(T_A + T_B) = m \times \frac{\sqrt{3}}{4} \times 4 \times 3g$$

$$T_A + T_B = 6mg \qquad \text{②}$$

$$\Rightarrow T_A = 4mg \,\text{N and } T_B = 2mg \,\text{N}$$

Simplify and solve the pair of simultaneous equations ① and ②.

Example 14

An aircraft of mass 2 tonnes flies at $500\,\text{km h}^{-1}$ on a path which follows a horizontal circular arc in order to change course from due north to due east. The aircraft turns in the clockwise direction from due north to due east. It takes 40 seconds to change course, with the aircraft banked at an angle α to the horizontal. Calculate the value of α and the magnitude of the lift force perpendicular to the surface of the aircraft's wings.

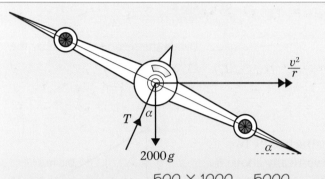

In normal flight the lift force acts vertically and balances the weight of the aircraft. By banking the aircraft the lift force is now doing two things: the vertical component is balancing the weight, and the horizontal component is the force which causes the acceleration towards the centre of the circular arc that the aircraft is to follow.

$$Speed = 500\,\text{km h}^{-1} = \frac{500 \times 1000}{3600} = \frac{5000}{36}\,\text{m s}^{-1}.$$

Convert the speed from km h^{-1} to m s^{-1}.

The aircraft completes one quarter of the circle in 40 seconds, so

$$40 \times \frac{5000}{36} = \frac{1}{4} \times 2\pi r$$

Distance travelled = speed × time.

$$r = \frac{40 \times 5000 \times 2}{36 \times \pi} \approx 3540\,\text{m}$$

Equate this to one quarter of the circumference of the circle to find the radius of the circle.

$$R(\rightarrow)\ \ T\sin\alpha = \frac{2000 \times \left(\frac{5000}{36}\right)^2}{3540} \approx 10\,908$$

Resolve towards the centre of the circle.

$$R(\uparrow):\ T\cos\alpha = 2000g \approx 19\,600$$

Resolve horizontally and vertically to form two equations in T and α.

$$\Rightarrow \tan\alpha = \frac{10\,908}{19\,600} \approx 0.557,\ \alpha \approx 29°$$

$$\text{and}\ T \approx \frac{19\,600}{\cos\alpha} = 22\,400\,\text{N}$$

Solve the simultaneous equations.

Exercise 4C

Whenever a numerical value of g is required take $g = 9.8\,\text{m s}^{-2}$.

1 A particle of mass 1.5 kg is attached to one end of a light inextensible string of length 60 cm. The other end of the string is attached to a fixed point A. The particle moves with constant angular speed in a horizontal circle of radius 36 cm. The centre of the circle is vertically below A. Calculate the tension in the string and the angular speed of the particle.

2 A particle of mass 750 g is attached to one end of a light inextensible string of length 0.7 m. The other end of the string is attached to a fixed point A. The particle moves with constant angular speed in a horizontal circle whose centre is 0.5 m vertically below A. Calculate the tension in the string and the angular speed of the particle.

3 A particle of mass 1.2 kg is attached to one end of a light inextensible string of length 2 m. The other end of the string is attached to a fixed point A. The particle moves in a horizontal circle with constant angular speed. The centre of the circle is vertically below A. The particle takes 2 seconds to complete one revolution. Calculate the tension in the string and the angle between the string and the vertical.

4 A conical pendulum consists of a light inextensible string AB of length 1 m, fixed at A and carrying a small ball of mass 6 kg at B. The particle moves in a horizontal circle, with centre vertically below A, at constant angular speed 3.5 rad s^{-1}. Find the tension in the string and the radius of the circle.

5 A conical pendulum consists of a light inextensible string AB of length l, fixed at A and carrying a small ball of mass m at B. The particle moves in a horizontal circle, with centre vertically below A, at constant angular speed ω. Find, in terms of m, l and ω, the tension in the string.

6 A conical pendulum consists of a light inextensible string AB fixed at A and carrying a small ball of mass m at B. With the string taut the particle moves in a horizontal circle at constant angular speed ω. The centre of the circle is at distance x vertically below A. Show that $\omega^2 x = g$.

7 A hemispherical bowl of radius r is resting in a fixed position with its rim horizontal. A particle P of mass m is moving in a horizontal circle around the smooth inside surface of the bowl.

The centre of the circle is $\frac{r}{3}$ below the centre of the bowl.

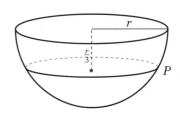

Find the angular speed of the particle and the magnitude of the reaction between the bowl and the particle.

8 A hemispherical bowl of radius r cm is resting in a fixed position with its rim horizontal. A small marble of mass m is moving in a horizontal circle around the smooth inside surface of the bowl. The plane of the circle is 3 cm below the plane of the rim of the bowl. Find the angular speed of the marble.

9 A hemispherical bowl of radius 15 cm is resting in a fixed position with its rim horizontal. A particle P of mass m is moving at 14 rad s^{-1} in a horizontal circle around the smooth inside surface of the bowl. Find the distance of the plane of the circle below the plane of the rim of the bowl.

10 A car travels round a bend of radius 750 m on a road which is banked at angle θ to the horizontal. The car is assumed to be moving at constant speed in a horizontal circle. If there is no frictional force acting on the car when it is travelling at 126 km h^{-1}, find the value of θ.

11 A car travels round a bend of radius 300 m on a road which is banked at an angle of 10° to the horizontal. The car is assumed to be moving at constant speed in a horizontal circle. At what speed does the car move if there is no frictional force?

12 A boy rides his cycle round a circular track of diameter 50 m. The track is banked at 20° to the horizontal. There is no force due to friction. By modelling the boy and his cycle as a particle of mass 75 kg, find the speed at which the cycle is moving.

13 A bend in the road is a horizontal circular arc of radius r. The surface of the bend is banked at an angle α to the horizontal. When a vehicle is driven round the bend there is no tendency to slip. Show that the speed of the vehicle is $\sqrt{rg \tan \alpha}$.

14 A girl rides her cycle round a circular track of diameter 60 m. The track is banked at 15° to the horizontal. The coefficient of friction between the track and the tyres of the cycle is 0.25. Modelling the girl and her cycle as a particle of mass 60 kg moving in a horizontal circle, find the minimum speed at which she can travel without slipping.

15 A van is moving on a horizontal circular bend in the road of radius 75 m. The bend is banked at $\tan^{-1}\frac{1}{3}$ to the horizontal. The maximum speed at which the van can be driven round the bend without slipping is 90 km h^{-1}. Calculate the coefficient of friction between the road surface and the tyres of the van.

16 A car moves on a horizontal circular path round a banked bend in a race track. The radius of the path is 100 m. The coefficient of friction between the car tyres and the track is 0.3. The maximum speed at which the car can be driven round the bend without slipping is 144 km h^{-1}. Find the angle at which the track is banked.

17 A bend in a race track is banked at 30°. A car will follow a horizontal circular path of radius 70 m round the bend. The coefficient of friction between the car tyres and the track surface is 0.4. Find the maximum and minimum speeds at which the car can be driven round the bend without slipping.

18 The diagram shows a small smooth ring R of mass 500 g threaded on a light inextensible string. The ends of the string are attached to fixed points A and B, where A is vertically above B. The string is taut and the system rotates about AB. The ring moves with constant angular speed on a horizontal circle of radius 0.6 m.

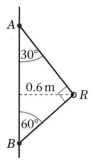

$\angle ABR = 60°$ and $\angle BAR = 30°$.
Modelling the ring as a particle, calculate the tension in the string and the angular speed of the particle.

19 A light elastic string AB has natural length 2 m and modulus of elasticity 30 N. The end A is attached to a fixed point. A particle of mass 750 g is attached to the end B. The particle is moving in a horizontal circle below A with the string inclined at 40° to the vertical. Find the angular speed of the particle.

20 An aircraft of mass 2 tonnes flies at $400\,\text{km}\,\text{h}^{-1}$ on a path which follows a horizontal circular arc in order to change course from a bearing of 060° to a bearing of 015°. It takes 25 seconds to change course, with the aircraft banked at $\alpha°$ to the horizontal. Calculate the two possible values of α and the corresponding values of the magnitude of the lift force perpendicular to the surface of the aircraft's wings.

4.4 You can use vector notation to describe motion in a circle.

A particle P is moving on a horizontal circular path at constant angular speed $\omega\,\text{rad}\,\text{s}^{-1}$.

The centre of the circle, O, is taken as the origin of perpendicular coordinate axes. The x-axis is the fixed direction from which the angle of the radius OP is measured.

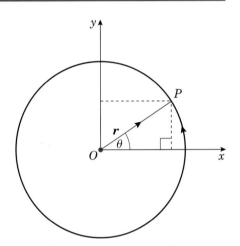

The unit vectors $\mathbf{i}$ and $\mathbf{j}$ are parallel to the x-axis and y-axis respectively.

In t seconds, OP turns through an angle ωt radians, so if P is on the x-axis at $t = 0$, the position vector of P after t seconds is given by

$$\mathbf{r} = r\cos\theta\,\mathbf{i} + r\sin\theta\,\mathbf{j}$$
$$= r\cos\omega t\,\mathbf{i} + r\sin\omega t\,\mathbf{j}$$

Exercise 4D

At time t seconds the position vector, relative to the centre of the circle, of a particle moving in a horizontal circle, centre O, at constant angular speed $\omega\,\text{rad}\,\text{s}^{-1}$ is given by

$$\mathbf{r} = r\cos\omega t\,\mathbf{i} + r\sin\omega t\,\mathbf{j}$$

1 **a** Differentiate $\mathbf{r}$ with respect to t to obtain the velocity, $\mathbf{v}$, of the particle.

   b Hence calculate the linear speed of the particle and deduce that $v = r\omega$.

2 **a** By considering the gradients of the vectors $\mathbf{r}$ and $\mathbf{v}$, or by taking the scalar product of $\mathbf{r}$ and $\mathbf{v}$, find the angle between these two vectors.

   b What does this tell you about the velocity of the particle?

3 **a** Differentiate $\mathbf{v}$ with respect to t to obtain the acceleration, $\mathbf{a}$, of the particle.

   b Express $\mathbf{a}$ in terms of $\mathbf{r}$. What does this tell you about the direction of the acceleration?

   c Calculate the magnitude of $\mathbf{a}$.

4.5 You can solve problems about objects moving in vertical circles.

When an object moves in a vertical circle it gains height as it follows its circular path. If it gains height then it must gain potential energy. Therefore, using the work–energy principle it follows that it must lose kinetic energy, and its speed will not be constant.

You can use vectors to understand motion in a vertical circle.

If O is the centre of the circle and P is the particle, we can set up coordinate axes in the plane of the circle with the x-axis horizontal, and the y-axis vertical.

Let the unit vectors $\mathbf{i}$ and $\mathbf{j}$ be parallel to the x-axis and y-axis respectively.

At time t the angle between the radius OP and the x-axis is θ and the position vector of P is $\mathbf{r}$.

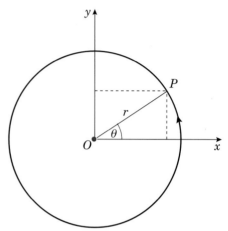

$$\mathbf{r} = (r\cos\theta)\mathbf{i} + (r\sin\theta)\mathbf{j}$$

By differentiating this with respect to time we obtain the velocity vector

$$\mathbf{v} = \frac{\mathrm{d}}{\mathrm{d}t}(\mathbf{r}) = (-r\sin\theta)\dot{\theta}\mathbf{i} + (r\cos\theta)\dot{\theta}\mathbf{j} = r\dot{\theta}(-\sin\theta\mathbf{i} + \cos\theta\mathbf{j})$$

Differentiating a second time we obtain the acceleration vector

$$\mathbf{a} = \frac{\mathrm{d}}{\mathrm{d}t}(\mathbf{v}) = ((-r\sin\theta)\ddot{\theta} + (-r\cos\theta)\dot{\theta}^2)\mathbf{i} + ((r\cos\theta)\ddot{\theta} + (-r\sin\theta)\dot{\theta}^2)\mathbf{j}$$

$$= -r\dot{\theta}^2(\cos\theta\mathbf{i} + \sin\theta\mathbf{j}) + r\ddot{\theta}(-\sin\theta\mathbf{i} + \cos\theta\mathbf{j})$$

Looking at the directions of $\mathbf{r}$ and $\mathbf{v}$, we find that the lines representing them have gradients $\dfrac{r\sin\theta}{r\cos\theta}$ and $-\dfrac{r\cos\theta}{r\sin\theta}$ respectively.

But $\dfrac{r\sin\theta}{r\cos\theta} \times \dfrac{r\cos\theta}{r\sin\theta} = -1$, so these two vectors are perpendicular. Alternatively, using the scalar product we see that the vectors are perpendicular since $(\cos\theta\mathbf{i} + \sin\theta\mathbf{j})\cdot(-\sin\theta\mathbf{i} + \cos\theta\mathbf{j}) = 0$.

This means that the acceleration has two components, one of magnitude $r\dot{\theta}^2$ directed towards the centre of the circle, and one of magnitude $r\ddot{\theta}$ directed along the tangent to the circle.

Using $\dot{\theta} = \omega$ gives:

■ **For motion in a vertical circle of radius r, the components of the acceleration are $r\omega^2$ towards the centre of the circle and $r\ddot{\theta} = \dot{v}$ along the tangent.**

The force directed towards the centre of the circle is perpendicular to the direction of motion of the particle, so it does no work. If the only other force acting on the particle is gravity, then it follows (using the work–energy principle) that the sum of the kinetic energy and the potential energy of the particle will be constant. You will use this fact to solve problems about motion in a vertical circle.

Example 15

A particle of mass 0.4 kg is attached to one end A of a light rod AB of length 0.3 m. The rod is free to rotate in a vertical plane about B. The particle is held at rest with AB horizontal. The particle is released. Calculate

a the speed of the particle as it passes through the lowest point of the path,

b the tension in the rod at this point.

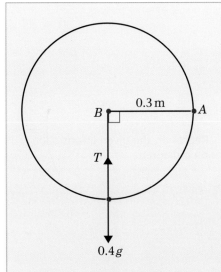

Represent the given information on a diagram.

Let the speed of the particle at the lowest point be $v\,\mathrm{m\,s^{-1}}$, and the tension in the rod be $T\,\mathrm{N}$.

a At the lowest point the particle has fallen a distance 0.3 m, so the P.E. lost $= 0.4 \times g \times 0.3$, and the K.E. gained $= \frac{1}{2} \times 0.4 \times v^2$.

Distance fallen is equal to the radius of the circle.

$$\therefore 0.4 \times g \times 0.3 = \frac{1}{2} \times 0.4 \times v^2$$

$$v^2 = 0.6 \times g \approx 5.88, \ v \approx 2.4\,\mathrm{m\,s^{-1}}$$

The particle was initially at rest.

b At the lowest point, the force towards the centre of the circle is given by

Using conservation of energy.

$$(\uparrow)T - 0.4\,g = \frac{0.4v^2}{0.3}$$

Resolve towards the centre of the circle.

$$\Rightarrow T = 0.4g + \frac{0.4 \times 0.6g}{0.3} = 1.2g \approx 11.8\,\mathrm{N}$$

Questions about motion in a vertical circle will often ask you to consider whether or not an object will perform complete circles. The next two examples illustrate the importance of considering how the circular motion occurs.

Example **16**

A particle of mass 0.4 kg is attached to one end A of a light rod AB of length 0.3 m. The rod is free to rotate in a vertical plane about B. The rod is hanging vertically with A below B when the particle is set in motion with a horizontal speed of u m s^{-1}. Find

a an expression for the speed of the particle when the rod is at an angle θ to the downward vertical through B,

b the minimum value of u for which the particle will perform a complete circle.

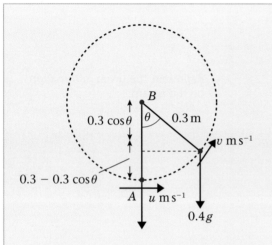

Represent the given information on a diagram.

a Take the lowest point of the circle as the zero level for potential energy.

You need to say which level you are measuring the P.E. from.

At the lowest level the particle has

$$\text{K.E.} = \tfrac{1}{2} \times 0.4 \times u^2 = 0.2u^2 \text{ J}$$

$$\text{P.E.} = 0 \text{ J}$$

When the rod is at angle θ to the vertical the particle has

$$\text{K.E.} = \tfrac{1}{2} \times 0.4 \times v^2 = 0.2v^2 \text{ J}$$

$$\text{P.E.} = 0.4 \times g \times 0.3(1 - \cos\theta) \text{ J}$$

$$\therefore 0.2u^2 = 0.2v^2 + 0.12g(1 - \cos\theta)$$

$$v = \sqrt{u^2 - 0.6g(1 - \cos\theta)}$$

Conservation of energy means that the total energy at each point will be equal.

b If the particle is to reach to top of the circle then we require $v > 0$ when $\theta = 180°$.

$$\Rightarrow u^2 - 0.6g(1 - \cos 180°) > 0$$

$$u^2 > 0.6g \times 2, \quad u > \sqrt{1.2g}$$

$\cos 180° = -1$

Note that if $u = \sqrt{1.2g}$ then the speed of the particle at the top of the circle would be zero. In this case the rod would be in thrust, with the force in the rod balancing the weight of the particle.

Example 17

A particle A of mass 0.4 kg is attached to one end of a light inextensible string of length 0.3 m. The other end of the string is attached to a fixed point B. The particle is hanging in equilibrium when it is set in motion with a horizontal speed of u m s^{-1}. Find

a an expression for the tension in the string when it is at an angle θ to the downward vertical through B,

b the minimum value of u for which the particle will perform a complete circle.

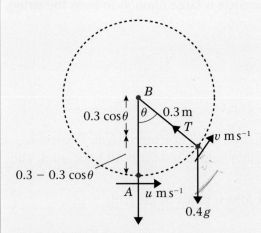

> Represent the given information on a diagram.

a Take the lowest point of the circle as the zero level for potential energy.

> You need to say which level you are measuring the P.E. from.

At the lowest level the particle has

$$K.E. = \tfrac{1}{2} \times 0.4 \times u^2 = 0.2u^2 \text{ J}$$
$$P.E. = 0 \text{ J}$$

When the rod is at angle θ to the vertical the particle has

$$K.E. = \tfrac{1}{2} \times 0.4 \times v^2 \text{ J}$$
$$P.E. = 0.4 \times g \times 0.3(1 - \cos\theta) \text{ J}$$
$$\therefore 0.2u^2 = 0.2v^2 + 0.12g(1 - \cos\theta)$$

Resolving towards the centre of the circle:

> Conservation of energy means that the total energy at each point will be equal.

$$(\nwarrow)T - 0.4g\cos\theta = \frac{mv^2}{r} = \frac{0.4v^2}{0.3}$$

> Use $a = \frac{v^2}{r}$.

$$T = 0.4g\cos\theta + \tfrac{4}{3}(u^2 - 0.6g + 0.6g\cos\theta)$$
$$= 1.2g\cos\theta + \frac{4u^2}{3} - 0.8g$$

> Express v^2 in terms of u^2.

b If the particle is to reach to top of the circle then we require $T > 0$ when $\theta = 180°$.

> If the particle is still on the circle then the string has not gone slack.

$$\Rightarrow -1.2g + \frac{4u^2}{3} - 0.8g > 0, \frac{4u^2}{3} > 2g$$

$$u^2 > \frac{6g}{4}, u > \sqrt{\frac{3g}{2}}$$

The difference between the two examples occurs because the rod can be supporting the particle (the force within the rod can be a thrust). This is not possible for the string.

■ **A particle attached to the end of a light rod will perform complete vertical circles if it has speed > 0 at the top of the circle.**

■ **A small bead threaded on to a smooth circular wire will perform complete vertical circles if it has speed > 0 at the top of the circle.**

■ **A particle attached to a light inextensible string will perform complete vertical circles if the speed of the particle when it reaches the top of the circle is large enough to keep the string taut at the top of the circle.**

Exercise 4E

Whenever a numerical value of g is required take $g = 9.8 \, \text{m s}^{-2}$.

1 A particle of mass 0.6 kg is attached to end A of a light rod AB of length 0.5 m. The rod is free to rotate in a vertical plane about B. The particle is held at rest with AB horizontal. The particle is released. Calculate

  a the speed of the particle as it passes through the lowest point of the path,

  b the tension in the rod at this point.

2 A particle of mass 0.4 kg is attached to end A of a light rod AB of length 0.3 m. The rod is free to rotate in a vertical plane about B. The particle is held at rest with A vertically above B. The rod is slightly displaced so that the particle moves in a vertical circle. Calculate

  a the speed of the particle as it passes through the lowest point of the path,

  b the tension in the rod at this point.

3 A particle of mass 0.4 kg is attached to end A of a light rod AB of length 0.3 m. The rod is free to rotate in a vertical plane about B. The particle is held at rest with AB at 60° to the upward vertical. The particle is released. Calculate

  a the speed of the particle as it passes through the lowest point of the path,

  b the tension in the rod at this point.

4 A particle of mass 0.6 kg is attached to end A of a light rod AB of length 0.5 m. The rod is free to rotate in a vertical plane about B. The particle is held at rest with AB at 60° to the upward vertical. The particle is released. Calculate

  a the speed of the particle as it passes through the point where AB is horizontal,

  b the tension in the rod at this point.

5 A particle of mass 0.5 kg is attached to end A of a light rod AB of length 0.7 m. The rod is free to rotate in a vertical plane about B. The particle is hanging with A vertically below B when it is projected horizontally with speed 10 m s⁻¹. Calculate

  a the speed of the particle when it is vertically above B,

  b the tension in the rod at this point.

6 A particle of mass 0.5 kg is attached to end A of a light rod AB of length 0.7 m. The rod is free to rotate in a vertical plane about B. The particle is hanging with A vertically below B when it is projected horizontally with speed u m s^{-1}. Find

a an expression in terms of u and θ for the speed of the particle when AB makes an angle of θ with the downward vertical through B,

b the restriction on u if the particle is to reach the highest point of the circle.

7 A particle A of mass 1.5 kg is attached to one end of a light inextensible string of length 2 m. The other end of the string is attached to a fixed point B. The particle is hanging in equilibrium when it is set in motion with a horizontal speed of u m s^{-1}. Find

a an expression for the tension in the string when it is at an angle θ to the downward vertical through B,

b the minimum value of u for which the particle will perform a complete circle.

8 A small bead of mass 50 g is threaded on a smooth circular wire of radius 75 cm which is fixed in a vertical plane. The bead is at rest at the lowest point of the wire when it is hit with an impulse of I N s horizontally causing it to start to move round the wire. Find the value of I if

a the bead just reaches the top of the circle,

b the bead just reaches the point where the radius from the bead to the centre of the circle makes an angle of $\tan^{-1}\frac{3}{4}$ with the upward vertical and then starts to slide back to its original position.

9 A particle of mass 50 g is attached to one end of a light inextensible string of length 75 cm. The other end of the string is attached to a fixed point. The particle is hanging at rest when it is hit with an impulse of I N s horizontally causing it to start to move in a vertical circle. Find the value of I if

a the particle just reaches the top of the circle,

b the string goes slack at the instant when the particle reaches the point where the string makes an angle of $\tan^{-1}\frac{3}{4}$ with the vertical.

10 A particle of mass 0.8 kg is attached to end A of a light rod AB of length 2 m. The end B is attached to a fixed point so that the rod is free to rotate in a vertical circle with its centre at B. The rod is held in a horizontal position and then released. Calculate the speed of the particle and the tension in the rod when

a the particle is at the lowest point of the circle,

b the rod makes an angle of $\tan^{-1}\frac{3}{4}$ with the downward vertical through B.

11 A particle of mass 500 g describes complete vertical circles on the end of a light inextensible string of length 1.5 m. Given that the speed of the particle is 8 m s^{-1} at the highest point, find

a the speed of the particle when the string is horizontal,

b the magnitude of the tangential acceleration when the string is horizontal,

c the tension in the string when the particle is at the lowest point of the circle.

12 A light rod AB of length 1 m has a particle of mass 4 kg attached at A. End B is pivoted to a fixed point so that AB is free to rotate in a vertical plane. When the rod is vertical with A below B the speed of the particle is $6.5\,\text{m s}^{-1}$. Find the angle between AB and the vertical at the instant when the tension in the rod is zero, and calculate the speed of the particle at that instant.

13 A particle P of mass m kg is attached to one end of a light rod of length r m which is free to rotate in a vertical plane about its other end. The particle describes complete vertical circles. Given that the tension at the lowest point of P's path is three times the tension at the highest point, find the speed of P at the lowest point on its path.

14 A particle P of mass m kg is attached to one end of a light inextensible string of length r m. The other end of the string is attached to a fixed point O, and P describes complete vertical circles about O. Given that the speed of the particle at the lowest point is one-and-a-half times the speed of the particle at the highest point, find

   a the speed of the particle at the highest point,

   b the tension in the string when the particle is at the highest point.

15 A light inelastic string of length r has one end attached to a fixed point O. A particle P of mass m kg is attached to the other end. P is held with OP horizontal and the string taut. P is then projected vertically downwards with speed $\sqrt{gr}$.

   a Find, in terms of θ, m and g, the tension in the string when OP makes an angle θ with the horizontal.

   b Given that the string will break when the tension in the string is $2mg$ N, find the angle between the string and the horizontal when the string breaks.

4.6 You can solve problems where an object does not have to stay on the circle.

In some models, for example a bead threaded on a ring or a particle attached to the end of a light rod, the object has to stay on the circular path. If the initial speed is not sufficient for the object to reach the top of the circular path then it will fall back and oscillate about the lowest point of the path. If an object is not constrained to stay on its circular path then as soon as the contact force associated with the circular path becomes zero the object can be treated as a projectile moving freely under gravity.

Example **18**

A particle P of mass m is attached to one end of a light inextensible string of length l. The other end of the string is attached to a fixed point O. The particle is hanging in equilibrium at point A, directly below O, when it is set in motion with a horizontal speed $2\sqrt{gl}$. When OP has turned through an angle θ and the string is still taut, the tension in the string is T.

a Find an expression for T.

b Find the height of P above A at the instant when the string goes slack.

c Find the maximum height above A reached by P before it starts to fall to the ground again.

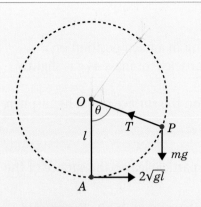

a When $\angle AOP = \theta$, P has speed v and the tension in the string is T.

Let A be the zero level for P.E.

Determine the level where P.E. = 0.

At A, P has P.E. $= 0$ and K.E. $= \frac{1}{2} \times m \times u^2 = \frac{1}{2} m \times 4gl$

When $\angle AOP = \theta$, P has P.E. $= mgl(1 - \cos \theta)$ and K.E. $= \frac{1}{2}mv^2$.

Find the total of P.E. $+$ K.E. at both levels.

$\therefore 2mgl = mgl(1 - \cos \theta) + \frac{1}{2}mv^2$

$$v^2 = 2gl(1 + \cos \theta)$$

Energy is conserved.

Resolving parallel to OP:

$$(\nwarrow)T - mg \cos \theta = \frac{mv^2}{l} = \frac{m \times 2gl(1 + \cos \theta)}{l}$$

Using the equation for circular motion.

$$\Rightarrow T = 2mg + 2mg \cos \theta + mg \cos \theta$$
$$= 2mg + 3mg \cos \theta$$

String slack, so $T = 0$.

b When $T = 0$, $\cos \theta = -\frac{2}{3}$, so the height of P above A is

$$l(1 - \cos \theta) = \frac{5l}{3}.$$

Substitute for $\cos \theta$.

c From the energy equation, we know that when the string becomes slack $v^2 = 2gl(1 + \cos \theta) = \frac{2gl}{3}$.

At this point the horizontal component of the velocity

$$= v \cos (180 - \theta) = \frac{2}{3}\sqrt{\frac{2gl}{3}}.$$

P is now moving freely under gravity. The horizontal component of the velocity will not change.
At the maximum height the vertical component of the velocity is zero

If the additional height before the particle begins to fall is h, then

$$mgh + \frac{1}{2} \times m \times \frac{4 \times 2gl}{9 \times 3} = \frac{1}{2} \times m \times v^2 = \frac{1 \times 2mgl}{2 \times 3},$$

Conservation of energy.

$$h = \frac{l}{3} - \frac{4l}{27} = \frac{5l}{27}$$

$\therefore$ total height above original level $= \frac{5l}{27} + \frac{5l}{3} = \frac{50l}{27}.$

This working does not imply that the particle is at maximum height when directly above A.

Example **19**

A smooth solid hemisphere with radius 5 m and centre O is resting in a fixed position on a horizontal plane with its flat face in contact with the plane. A particle P of mass 4 kg is slightly disturbed from rest at the highest point of the hemisphere.

When OP has turned through an angle θ and the particle is still on the surface of the hemisphere the normal reaction of the sphere on the particle is R.

a Find an expression for R.

b Find the angle between OP and the upward vertical when the particle leaves the surface of the hemisphere.

c Find the distance of the particle from the centre of the hemisphere when it hits the ground.

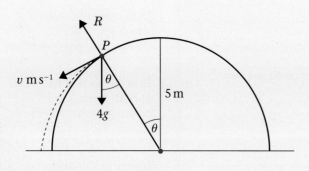

| | Draw and label a diagram. |

a Let the horizontal plane be the level of zero P.E.

At the top of the hemisphere, K.E. = 0 and
P.E. = $4 \times g \times 5 = 20g$.

> Choose a zero level for P.E.

When OP is at an angle θ to the upward vertical,

$$\text{K.E.} = \tfrac{1}{2}mv^2 = 2v^2$$

$$\text{P.E.} = 4 \times g \times 5\cos\theta = 20g\cos\theta$$

> Find the total of P.E. + K.E. at both points.

$$\therefore 20g = 2v^2 + 20g\cos\theta$$

$$v^2 = 10g(1 - \cos\theta)$$

> Energy is conserved.

Resolving parallel to PO:

$$(\searrow)\, 4g\cos\theta - R = \frac{mv^2}{r} = \frac{4 \times 10g(1 - \cos\theta)}{5}$$

$$= 8g(1 - \cos\theta)$$

> Use the equation for circular motion and substitute for v^2.

so $R = 4g\cos\theta - 8g + 8g\cos\theta = 12g\cos\theta - 8g$

b The particle leaves the hemisphere when $R = 0$.

This is when $\cos\theta = \tfrac{2}{3}$

$$\theta = \cos^{-1}\tfrac{2}{3} \approx 48°$$

> The particle leaves the hemisphere when there is no contact force.

c When the particle leaves the hemisphere:

vertical distance $OP = 5\cos\theta = \frac{10}{3}$

horizontal distance $OP = 5\sin\theta = \frac{5\sqrt{5}}{3}$

and $v^2 = 10g\left(1 - \frac{2}{3}\right) = \frac{10g}{3}$

initial vertical speed $\sqrt{\frac{10g}{3}} \times \frac{\sqrt{5}}{3}$, so

$\frac{10}{3} = \sqrt{\frac{50g}{27}}\,t + \frac{1}{2}gt^2$

$3\sqrt{3}gt^2 + 2\sqrt{50g}\,t - 20\sqrt{3} = 0$

$t = 0.4976\ldots$

Horizontal distance travelled in this time

$= v\cos\theta \times t = \sqrt{\frac{10g}{3}} \times \frac{2}{3} \times 0.4976\ldots = 1.897\ldots$

Total distance from $O = \frac{5\sqrt{5}}{3} + 1.897\ldots \approx 5.6\,\text{m}$

> The particle is now a projectile with initial speed $\sqrt{\frac{10g}{3}}$ at an angle $\cos^{-1}\frac{2}{3}$ below the horizontal.

> Using $s = ut + \frac{1}{2}at^2$ and solving the quadratic equation for t.

> No horizontal acceleration.

> Add the two horizontal distances.

Exercise 4F

Whenever a numerical value of g is required take $g = 9.8\,\text{m s}^{-2}$.

1 A particle P of mass m is attached to one end of a light inextensible string of length l. The other end of the string is attached to a fixed point O. The particle is hanging in equilibrium at a point A, directly below O, when it is set in motion with a horizontal speed $\sqrt{3gl}$.

When OP has turned through an angle θ and the string is still taut, the tension in the string is T.

a Find an expression for T.

b Find the height of P above A at the instant when the string goes slack.

c Find the maximum height above A reached by P before it starts to fall to the ground again.

2 A smooth solid hemisphere with radius 6 m and centre O is resting in a fixed position on a horizontal plane with its flat face in contact with the plane. A particle P of mass 3 kg is slightly disturbed from rest at the highest point of the hemisphere.

When OP has turned through an angle θ and the particle is still on the surface of the hemisphere the normal reaction of the sphere on the particle is R.

a Find an expression for R.

b Find the angle between OP and the upward vertical when the particle leaves the surface of the hemisphere.

c Find the distance of the particle from the centre of the hemisphere when it hits the ground.

3 A smooth solid hemisphere is fixed with its plane face on a horizontal table and its curved surface uppermost. The plane face of the hemisphere has centre O and radius r. The point A is the highest point on the hemisphere. A particle P is placed on the hemisphere at A. It is then given an initial horizontal speed u, where $u^2 = \dfrac{rg}{4}$. When OP makes an angle θ with OA, and while P remains on the hemisphere, the speed of P is v.

a Find an expression for v^2.

b Find the value of $\cos \theta$ when P leaves the hemisphere.

c Find the value of v when P leaves the hemisphere.

After leaving the hemisphere P strikes the table at B.

d Find the speed of P at B.

e Find the angle at which P strikes the table.

4 A smooth sphere with centre O and radius $2\,\text{m}$ is fixed to a horizontal surface. A particle P of mass $3\,\text{kg}$ is slightly disturbed from rest at the highest point of the sphere and starts to slide down the surface of the sphere.

a Find the angle between OP and the upward vertical at the instant when P leaves the surface of the sphere.

b Find the magnitude and direction of the velocity of the particle as it hits the horizontal surface.

5 A particle of mass m is projected with speed v from the top of the outside of a smooth sphere of radius a. In the subsequent motion the particle slides down the surface of the sphere and leaves the surface of the sphere with speed $\dfrac{\sqrt{3ga}}{2}$.

a Find the vertical distance travelled by the particle before it loses contact with the surface of the sphere.

b Find v.

c Find the magnitude and direction of the velocity of the particle when it is at the same horizontal level as the centre of the sphere.

6 A smooth hemisphere with centre O and radius $50\,\text{cm}$ is fixed with its plane face in contact with a horizontal surface. A particle P is released from rest at point A on the sphere, where OA is inclined at $10°$ to the upward vertical. The particle leaves the sphere at point B. Find the angle between OB and the upward vertical.

7 A smooth laundry chute is built in two sections, PQ and QR. Each section is in the shape of an arc of a circle. PQ has radius 5 m and subtends an angle of 70° at its centre, A. QR has radius 7 m and subtends an angle of 40° at its centre, B. The points A, Q and B are in a vertical straight line. The laundry bags are collected in a large bin $\frac{1}{2}$ m below R. To test the chute, a small particle of mass 2 kg is released from rest at P.

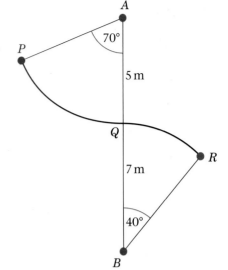

   a Calculate the speed with which the particle reaches the bin at the bottom of the chute.

   b Determine whether or not the particle loses contact with the chute before it reaches R.

8 Part of a hollow spherical shell, centre O and radius a, is removed to form a bowl with a plane circular rim. The bowl is fixed with the rim uppermost and horizontal. The centre of the circular rim is $\frac{4a}{3}$ vertically above the lowest point of the bowl. A marble is projected from the lowest point of the bowl with speed u. Find the minimum value of u for which the marble will leave the bowl and not fall back in to it.

Mixed exercise 4G

1 A particle of mass m moves with constant speed u in a horizontal circle of radius $\frac{3a}{2}$ on the inside of a fixed smooth hollow sphere of radius $2a$. Show that $9ag = 2\sqrt{7}u^2$.

2

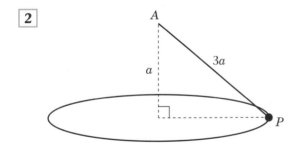

A particle P of mass m is attached to one end of a light inextensible string of length $3a$. The other end of the string is attached to a fixed point A which is a vertical distance a above a smooth horizontal table. The particle moves on the table in a circle whose centre O is vertically below A, as shown in the diagram. The string is taut and the speed of P is $2\sqrt{ag}$. Find

   a the tension in the string,

   b the normal reaction of the table on P.

3

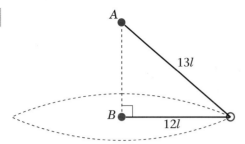

A light inextensible string of length 25*l* has its ends fixed to two points *A* and *B*, where *A* is vertically above *B*. A small smooth ring of mass *m* is threaded on the string. The ring is moving with constant speed in a horizontal circle with centre *B* and radius 12*l*, as shown in the diagram. Find

a the tension in the string,

b the speed of the ring.

4 A car moves round a bend which is banked at a constant angle of 12° to the horizontal. When the car is travelling at a constant speed of 15 m s⁻¹ there is no sideways frictional force on the car. The car is modelled as a particle moving in a horizontal circle of radius *r* metres. Calculate the value of *r*.

5

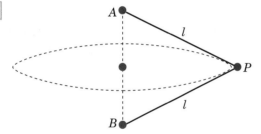

A particle *P* of mass *m* is attached to the ends of two light inextensible strings *AP* and *BP* each of length *l*. The ends *A* and *B* are attached to fixed points, with *A* vertically above *B* and *AB = l*, as shown in the diagram. The particle *P* moves in a horizontal circle with constant angular speed ω. The centre of the circle is the mid-point of *AB* and both strings remain taut.

a Show that the tension in *AP* is $\frac{m}{2}(2g + l\omega^2)$.

b Find, in terms of *m*, *l*, ω and *g*, an expression for the tension in *BP*.

c Deduce that $\omega^2 > \frac{2g}{l}$.

6

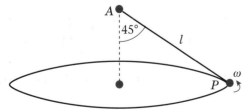

A particle *P* of mass *m* is attached to one end of a light string of length *l*. The other end of the string is attached to a fixed point *A*. The particle moves in a horizontal circle with constant angular speed ω and with the string inclined at an angle of 45° to the vertical, as shown in the diagram.

a Show that the tension in the string is $\sqrt{2}mg$.

b Find ω in terms of g and l.

7 A rough disc rotates in a horizontal plane with constant angular velocity ω about a fixed vertical axis. A particle P of mass m lies on the disc at a distance $\frac{3}{5}a$ from the axis. The coefficient of friction between P and the disc is $\frac{3}{7}$. Given that P remains at rest relative to the disc,

a prove that $\omega^2 \leqslant \dfrac{5g}{7a}$.

The particle is now connected to the axis by a horizontal light elastic string of natural length $\frac{a}{2}$ and modulus of elasticity $\dfrac{5mg}{2}$. The disc again rotates with constant angular velocity ω about the axis and P remains at rest relative to the disc at a distance $\frac{3}{5}a$ from the axis.

b Find the range of possible values of ω^2.

8 A particle P of mass $0.6\,\text{kg}$ is attached to one end of a light inextensible string of length $1.2\,\text{m}$. The other end of the string is attached to a fixed point A. The particle is moving, with the string taut, in a horizontal circle with centre O vertically below A. The particle is moving with constant angular speed $3\,\text{rad s}^{-1}$. Find

a the tension in the string,

b the angle between AP and the downward vertical.

9 A particle P of mass m moves on the smooth inner surface of a spherical bowl of internal radius r. The particle moves with constant angular speed in a horizontal circle, which is at a depth $\frac{r}{4}$ below the centre of the bowl. Find

a the normal reaction of the bowl on P,

b the time it takes P to complete three revolutions of its circular path.

10

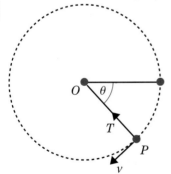

A particle P of mass m is attached to one end of a light inextensible string of length a. The other end of the string is fixed at a point O. The particle is held with the string taut and OP horizontal. It is then projected vertically downwards with speed u, where $u^2 = \frac{4}{3}ga$. When OP has turned through an angle θ and the string is still taut, the speed of P is v and the tension in the string is T, as shown in the diagram.

a Find an expression for v^2 in terms of a, g and θ.

b Find an expression for T in terms of m, g and θ.

c Find, to the nearest degree, the value of θ when the string becomes slack.

d Explain why P would not complete a vertical circle if the string were replaced by a light rod.

11 A particle P of mass $0.4\,\text{kg}$ is attached to one end of a light inelastic string of length $1\,\text{m}$. The other end of the string is fixed at point O. P is hanging in equilibrium below O when it is projected horizontally with speed $u\,\text{m s}^{-1}$. When OP is horizontal it meets a small smooth peg at Q, where $OQ = 0.8\,\text{m}$. Calculate the minimum value of u if P is to describe a complete circle about Q.

12 A smooth solid hemisphere is fixed with its plane face on a horizontal table and its curved surface uppermost. The plane face of the hemisphere has centre O and radius a. The point A is the highest point on the hemisphere. A particle P is placed on the hemisphere at A.

It is then given an initial horizontal speed u, where $u^2 = \dfrac{ag}{2}$. When OP makes an angle θ with OA, and while P remains on the hemisphere, the speed of P is v.

a Find an expression for v^2.

b Show that P is still on the hemisphere when $\theta = \cos^{-1}0.9$

c Find the value of **i** $\cos\theta$ when P leaves the hemisphere,

             ii v when P leaves the hemisphere.

After leaving the hemisphere P strikes the table at B.

d Find the speed of P at B.

e Find the angle at which P strikes the table.

13 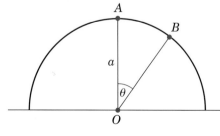 Part of a hollow spherical shell, centre O and radius r, is removed to form a bowl with a plane circular rim. The bowl is fixed with the circular rim uppermost and horizontal. The point C is the lowest point of the bowl. The point B is on the rim of the bowl and OB is at an angle α to the upward vertical as shown in the diagram. Angle α satisfies $\tan\alpha = \frac{4}{3}$. A smooth small marble of mass m is placed inside the bowl at C and given an initial horizontal speed u. The direction of motion of the marble lies in the vertical plane COB. The marble stays in contact with the bowl until it reaches B. When the marble reaches B it has speed v.

a Find an expression for v^2.

b If $u^2 = 4gr$, find the normal reaction of the bowl on the marble as the marble reaches B.

c Find the least possible value of u for the marble to reach B.

The point A is the other point of the rim of the bowl lying in the vertical plane COB.

d Find the value of u which will enable the marble to leave the bowl at B and meet it again at A.

14 A particle is at the highest point A on the outer surface of a fixed smooth hemisphere of radius a and centre O. The hemisphere is fixed to a horizontal surface with the plane face in contact with the surface. The particle is projected horizontally from A with speed u, where $u < \sqrt{ag}$. The particle leaves the sphere at the point B, where OB makes an angle θ with the upward vertical, as shown in the diagram.

a Find an expression for $\cos \theta$ in terms of u, g and a.

The particle strikes the horizontal surface with speed $\sqrt{\dfrac{5ag}{2}}$.

b Find the value of θ.

Summary of key points

1 If a particle is moving around a circle of radius r m with linear speed v m s^{-1} and angular speed ω rad s^{-1} then $v = r\omega$.

2 The acceleration of an object moving round a circle of radius r at constant speed is $r\omega^2$, or $\dfrac{v^2}{r}$, towards the centre of the circle.

3 For motion in a vertical circle of radius r, the components of the acceleration are $r\omega^2 = \dfrac{v^2}{r}$ towards the centre of the circle and $r\ddot{\theta} = \dot{v}$ along the tangent.

4 A particle moving in a vertical circle will be subject to a resultant force directed towards the centre of the circle. If the only force doing work on the particle is gravity, then the total energy (i.e. kinetic energy + potential energy) of the particle will remain constant as it moves round the circle.

5 If a particle is constrained to move on a vertical circle, i.e. it *cannot* move out of the circle, for example a particle attached to the end of a light rod which is rotating in a vertical circle or a particle threaded on to a smooth circular wire which is fixed in a vertical plane then the particle will perform complete vertical circles if it has speed > 0 at the top of the circle.

6 If a particle is *not* constrained to move on a vertical circle, i.e. it *can* move off the circle, for example, a particle attached to the end of a light string which is rotating in a vertical plane or a particle moving in a vertical circle on the inside of a fixed sphere, then the particle will perform complete circles if the speed of the particle is large enough when it reaches the top of the circle to keep the string taut at the top of the circle or make the normal reaction from the sphere > 0.

After completing this chapter you should be able to:

* use calculus to find the centre of mass of a uniform plane lamina
* find the centre of mass of a uniform solid body
* consider simple cases of equilibrium of rigid bodies
* determine whether a body is about to slip or is about to topple.

Statics of rigid bodies

In M2 you found the centre of mass of a uniform plane lamina using its symmetries. In this section you will learn a more general method of establishing the position of the centre of mass, which is not dependent on symmetry and uses calculus.

You will also consider the equilibrium of rigid bodies and determine whether such a body is about to topple.

The leaning tower of Pisa has not toppled over despite a lean of approximately five degrees from the vertical. This is because engineers have been able to calculate methods to prevent this from happening.

5.1 You can find the centre of mass of a lamina using calculus.

In book M2, Chapter 2, you found the centre of mass of a uniform plane lamina by using symmetries and standard formulae.

■ $\sum m_i x_i = \bar{x} \sum m_i$ and $\sum m_i y_i = \bar{y} \sum m_i$.

You used these results to find the centre of mass of a composite lamina. In Example 1 you will obtain a general result, which uses calculus to find the position of a centre of mass.

Example 1

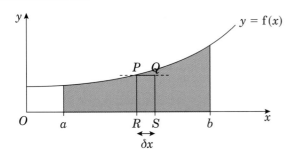

Find the centre of mass of the uniform lamina bounded by the curve with equation $y = \mathrm{f}(x)$, the x-axis, and the lines $x = a$ and $x = b$. This lamina is shown shaded in the figure.

Consider the lamina as made up of small rectangular strips such as PQSR, parallel to the y-axis. Let P have coordinates (x, y) and let the width of the strip be δx.

> δx is small and so PQSR is almost a rectangle.

The height of the strip is y and its area is $y\,\delta x$.

The mass of the strip (m_i) is $\rho y\,\delta x$, where ρ is the mass per unit area of the lamina.

As the strip is a rectangle, the coordinates of its centre of mass are $(x, \frac{1}{2}y)$.

> This is obtained from symmetry and is only true if δx is small.

Let the coordinates of the centre of mass of the lamina be at the point $(\bar{x}, \bar{y})$.

As $\sum m_i x_i = \bar{x} \sum m_i$, $\displaystyle\sum_{x=a}^{x=b} (\rho y\,\delta x)\,x = \bar{x} \sum_{x=a}^{x=b} \rho y\,\delta x$

> This was a key point in M2, Chapter 2.

And so $\bar{x} = \dfrac{\displaystyle\sum_{x=a}^{x=b} (\rho y\,\delta x)\,x}{\displaystyle\sum_{x=a}^{x=b} \rho y\,\delta x}$

As $\delta x \rightarrow 0$ the summations become integrals and

$$\bar{x} = \frac{\int_a^b xy\,dx}{\int_a^b y\,dx} = \frac{\int_a^b xf(x)\,dx}{\int_a^b f(x)\,dx}$$

> Repeat the process to find the y-coordinate of the centre of mass.

Also $\sum m_i y_i = \bar{y}\sum m_i,\ \sum_{x=a}^{x=b}(\rho y\,\delta x)\dfrac{y}{2} = \bar{y}\sum_{x=a}^{x=b}\rho y\,\delta x$

And so $\bar{y} = \dfrac{\displaystyle\sum_{x=a}^{x=b}(\rho y\,\delta x)\dfrac{y}{2}}{\displaystyle\sum_{x=a}^{x=b}\rho y\,\delta x}$

As $\delta x \rightarrow 0$ the summations become integrals and

$$\bar{y} = \frac{\int_a^b \frac{1}{2}y^2\,dx}{\int_a^b y\,dx} = \frac{\int_a^b \frac{1}{2}f(x)^2\,dx}{\int_a^b f(x)\,dx}$$

■ **The centre of mass of a lamina may be found using the formulae**

- $$\bar{x} = \frac{\int_a^b xy\,dx}{\int_a^b y\,dx} \text{ and } \bar{y} = \frac{\int_a^b \frac{1}{2}y^2\,dx}{\int_a^b y\,dx}$$

- $M\bar{x} = \int_a^b \rho xy\,dx$ and $M\bar{y} = \int_a^b \frac{1}{2}\rho y^2\,dx$, where $M = \int_a^b \rho y\,dx$, **and is the total mass of the lamina.**

Example 2

Use calculus to find the position of the centre of mass of a right angled triangular lamina OPQ with base b and height h, as shown in the figure.

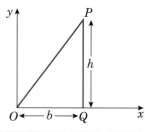

The equation of OP is $y = \dfrac{h}{b}x$

The mass M of the triangular lamina
$$= \rho \times \text{area} = \rho \times \tfrac{1}{2}bh$$

Using the formula for $\bar{x}$, $M\bar{x} = \int_a^b \rho xy\,dx$

$$M\bar{x} = \int_0^b \rho x\frac{h}{b}x\,dx = \frac{h}{b}\rho\int_0^b x^2\,dx$$

$$= \frac{h}{b}\rho\left[\frac{1}{3}x^3\right]_0^b = \frac{1}{3}\rho hb^2$$

So $\bar{x} = \dfrac{\frac{1}{3}\rho hb^2}{\frac{1}{2}\rho hb} = \dfrac{2}{3}b$

> Find the equation of the line OP by calculating the gradient of OP and using $y = mx + c$, with $c = 0$.

> Use area of triangle formula and let the mass per unit area be ρ.

> Use the formulae for the centre of mass of a lamina to find $\bar{x}$ and $\bar{y}$.

Also $M\bar{y} = \int_a^b \frac{1}{2}\rho y^2\,dx = \int_a^b \frac{1}{2}\rho\left(\frac{h}{b}x\right)^2 dx$

$$= \frac{1}{2}\rho\left(\frac{h}{b}\right)^2\left[\frac{1}{3}x^3\right]_0^b = \frac{1}{6}\rho h^2 b$$

So $\bar{y} = \dfrac{\frac{1}{6}\rho h^2 b}{\frac{1}{2}\rho hb} = \dfrac{1}{3}h$

So the centre of mass is at the point $\left(\frac{2}{3}b, \frac{1}{3}h\right)$.

Notice that the centre of mass is at
$$\left(\frac{x_1 + x_2 + x_3}{3}, \frac{y_1 + y_2 + y_3}{3}\right),$$
i.e. $\left(\dfrac{0 + b + b}{3}, \dfrac{0 + 0 + a}{3}\right)$ as given in M2.

Example 3

Find the coordinates of the centre of mass of the uniform lamina bounded by the curve with equation $y = 4 - x^2$ the x-axis and the y-axis, as shown.

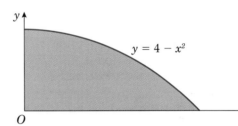

$y = 4 - x^2$

The curve meets the x-axis when $x = 2$.

$$\bar{x} = \frac{\int_0^b xy\,dx}{\int_0^b y\,dx} = \frac{\int_0^2 x(4 - x^2)\,dx}{\int_0^2 (4 - x^2)\,dx}$$

Put $y = 0$ and solve $4 - x^2 = 0$ to obtain $x = 2$.

$$\int_0^2 x(4 - x^2)\,dx = \int_0^2 (4x - x^3)\,dx$$
$$= \left[2x^2 - \frac{1}{4}x^4\right]_0^2 = 8 - 4 = 4$$

Substitute $y = 4 - x^2$ into the formula for $\bar{x}$.

$$\int_0^2 4 - x^2\,dx = \left[4x - \frac{1}{3}x^3\right]_0^2$$
$$= 8 - \frac{8}{3} = 5\frac{1}{3}$$

So $\bar{x} = \dfrac{4}{5\frac{1}{3}} = \dfrac{3}{4}$

Integrate and evaluate $\bar{x}$.

$$\bar{y} = \frac{\int_a^b \frac{1}{2}y^2\,dx}{\int_a^b y\,dx} = \frac{\int_0^2 \frac{1}{2}(4 - x^2)^2\,dx}{\int_0^2 (4 - x^2)\,dx}$$

Substitute $y = 4 - x^2$ into the formula for $\bar{y}$.

$$\int_0^2 \frac{1}{2}(4 - x^2)^2\,dx = \frac{1}{2}\int_0^2 16 - 8x^2 + x^4\,dx$$
$$= \frac{1}{2}\left[16x - \frac{8}{3}x^3 + \frac{1}{5}x^5\right]_0^2$$
$$= \frac{1}{2}\left(32 - \frac{64}{3} + \frac{32}{5}\right) = 8\frac{8}{15}$$

Integrate and evaluate $\bar{y}$.

So $\bar{y} = \dfrac{8\frac{8}{15}}{5\frac{1}{3}} = 1\frac{3}{5}$

The coordinates of the centre of mass are at $\left(\frac{3}{4}, 1\frac{3}{5}\right)$.

Example 4

A uniform semi-circular lamina has radius r cm. Find the position of its centre of mass.

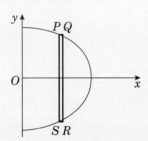

Take the diameter of the lamina as the y-axis, and the mid-point of the diameter as the origin. Let $PQRS$ be an elemental strip with width δx, where P has coordinates (x, y).

The centre of mass of this strip is at the point $(x, 0)$

> The width of the strip may be ignored as it is small.

The centre of mass of all such strips is on the x-axis and so the centre of mass of the lamina is also on the x-axis. This is the axis of symmetry of the lamina.

As point P lies on the circumference of the circle radius r, $x^2 + y^2 = r^2$, and so $y = \sqrt{r^2 - x^2}$.

The area of the strip is $2y\,\delta x$ and so its mass is $2\rho y\,\delta x$, where ρ is the mass per unit area of the lamina.

> Note that the length of the strip is $2y$, due to the symmetry of the semi-circle.

The mass M of the lamina is $\frac{1}{2}\pi r^2 \rho$ and $\bar{x}$ is obtained from

> The area of the semi-circle is $\frac{1}{2}\pi r^2$.

$$M\bar{x} = \int_0^r 2\rho x \sqrt{(r^2 - x^2)}\, dx$$

$$= \rho \int_0^r 2x(r^2 - x^2)^{\frac{1}{2}}\, dx$$

$$= \rho\left[-\tfrac{2}{3}\left[r^2 - x^2\right]^{\frac{3}{2}}\right]_0^r$$

> The integration may be done by substitution or by inspection using the chain rule in reverse.

$$= \tfrac{2}{3}\rho r^3$$

$$\text{So } \bar{x} = \frac{\tfrac{2}{3}\rho r^3}{\tfrac{1}{2}\rho \pi r^2} = \frac{4r}{3\pi}$$

> This result should be learned and may be quoted unless you are asked to derive it using calculus.

The centre of mass is on the axis of symmetry at a distance of $\dfrac{4r}{3\pi}$ from the straight edge diameter.

Example 5

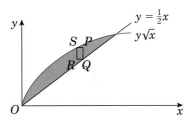

The figure shows a uniform lamina occupying the finite shaded region bounded by the curve with equation $y = \sqrt{x}$, and the straight line with equation $y = \frac{1}{2}x$. Find the coordinates of the centre of mass of the lamina.

Consider an elemental strip such as PQRS, where P is the point (x, y_1), which lies on the curve $y = \sqrt{x}$, and Q is the point (x, y_2), which lies on the line $y = \frac{1}{2}x$.

The area of the strip is $(y_1 - y_2)\,\delta x$ and its mass is $\rho(y_1 - y_2)\,\delta x$ where ρ is the mass per unit area of the lamina.

> δx is the width of the strip.

The centre of mass of the strip lies at the point $\left(x, \frac{1}{2}(y_1 + y_2)\right)$

The line meets the curve when $\sqrt{x} = \frac{1}{2}x$, i.e. when $x = 0$ and $x = 4$.

> Square both sides and solve the resulting quadratic equation $x = \frac{1}{4}x^2$.

The mass M of the lamina is given by

$$M = \int_a^b \rho(y_1 - y_2)\,dx = \rho\int_0^4 \sqrt{x} - \tfrac{1}{2}x\,dx$$

> Sum the strips and let $\delta x \to 0$. The summations become integrals and you obtain this result.

So $M = \rho\left[\frac{2}{3}x^{\frac{3}{2}} - \frac{x^2}{4}\right]_0^4 = \rho\left(\frac{16}{3} - \frac{16}{4}\right) = \frac{4}{3}\rho$

Using $M\bar{x} = \int_a^b \rho x(y_1 - y_2)\,dx = \rho\int_0^4 x^{\frac{3}{2}} - \frac{1}{2}x^2\,dx$

> Use $M\bar{x} = \sum_{x=a}^{x=b} \rho x(y_1 - y_2)\,\delta x$
> and let $\delta x \to 0$, so that the summation becomes an integral.

$$= \rho\left[\frac{2}{5}x^{\frac{5}{2}} - \frac{x^3}{6}\right]_0^4 = \rho\left(\frac{64}{5} - \frac{64}{6}\right) = \frac{64}{30}\rho$$

So $\bar{x} = \frac{64}{30} \times \frac{3}{4} = \frac{8}{5}$ or 1.6

> Divide $\frac{64}{30}\rho$ by $\frac{4}{3}\rho$, as $m = \frac{4}{3}\rho$.

Using $M\bar{y} = \int_a^b \frac{1}{2}\rho(y_1 + y_2)(y_1 - y_2)\,dx$

> Use
> $$M\bar{y} = \sum_{x=a}^{x=b} \rho\frac{y_1 + y_2}{2}(y_1 - y_2)\,\delta x$$
> and let $\delta x \to 0$, so that the summation becomes an integral.

$$= \frac{1}{2}\rho\int_0^4 \left(\sqrt{x} + \tfrac{1}{2}x\right)\left(\sqrt{x} - \tfrac{1}{2}x\right)dx$$

$$= \frac{1}{2}\rho\int_0^4 x - \tfrac{1}{4}x^2\,dx$$

$$= \frac{1}{2}\rho\left[\frac{1}{2}x^2 - \frac{x^3}{12}\right]_0^4 = \frac{1}{2}\rho\left(8 - \frac{64}{12}\right) = \frac{4}{3}\rho$$

So $\bar{y} = \frac{4}{3} \times \frac{3}{4} = 1$

> Divide $\frac{4}{3}\rho$ by $\frac{4}{3}\rho$, as $M = \frac{4}{3}\rho$.

The centre of mass is at the point (1.6, 1).

Example 6

A metallic badge is formed by removing three semi-circles of radius 1 cm from a larger semi-circle of radius 3 cm. The resulting shape is shown in the diagram.

Find the centre of mass of the badge, assuming that it is a uniform lamina.

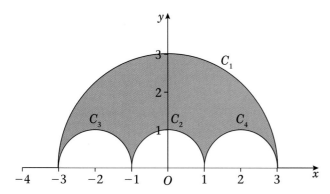

This question can be answered using M2 techniques.

List the shapes with their masses and the positions of their centres of mass in a table:

Shape	Mass	Centre of mass
Large semi-circle C_1	$\dfrac{9\pi}{2}\rho$	$\left(0, \dfrac{12}{3\pi}\right)$
Small semi-circle C_2	$\dfrac{\pi}{2}\rho$	$\left(0, \dfrac{4}{3\pi}\right)$
Small semi-circle C_3	$\dfrac{\pi}{2}\rho$	$\left(-2, \dfrac{4}{3\pi}\right)$
Small semi-circle C_4	$\dfrac{\pi}{2}\rho$	$\left(2, \dfrac{4}{3\pi}\right)$
Whole shape	$3\pi\rho$	$(\bar{x}, \bar{y})$

Use the result $\dfrac{4r}{3\pi}$, obtained in Example 4.

List the masses and the positions of the centres of mass in a table.

Then $\dfrac{9\pi}{2}\rho\begin{pmatrix} 0 \\ \frac{12}{3\pi} \end{pmatrix} - \dfrac{\pi}{2}\rho\begin{pmatrix} 0 \\ \frac{4}{3\pi} \end{pmatrix} - \dfrac{\pi}{2}\rho\begin{pmatrix} -2 \\ \frac{4}{3\pi} \end{pmatrix} - \dfrac{\pi}{2}\rho\begin{pmatrix} 2 \\ \frac{4}{3\pi} \end{pmatrix} = 3\pi\rho\begin{pmatrix} \bar{x} \\ \bar{y} \end{pmatrix}$

Use $\sum m_i \mathbf{r}_i = \bar{\mathbf{r}}\sum m_i$.

So $\begin{pmatrix} 0 \\ 18\rho - \frac{2}{3}\rho - \frac{2}{3}\rho - \frac{2}{3}\rho \end{pmatrix} = 3\pi\rho\begin{pmatrix} \bar{x} \\ \bar{y} \end{pmatrix}$

So $\bar{x} = 0$, $\bar{y} = \dfrac{16}{3\pi}$

The centre of mass is at a distance $\dfrac{16}{3\pi}$ from O along the line of symmetry.

Example 7

Find the centre of mass of a uniform lamina in the form of a sector of a circle, radius r and centre O, which subtends an angle 2α at O.

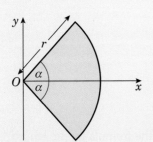 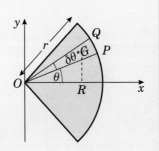

Divide the lamina into elements such as OPQ, which is a sector subtending an angle $\delta\theta$ at O. •——

The area of OPQ is $\frac{1}{2}r^2\,\delta\theta$ and its mass is $\frac{1}{2}r^2\rho\,\delta\theta$

The sector is approximately a triangle and so its centre of mass, G, is at a distance $\frac{2}{3}r$ from O.
The distance marked OR on the diagram is $\frac{2}{3}r\cos\theta$.•

The mass M of the whole sector is

$$\rho \times \tfrac{1}{2}r^2 2\alpha = \rho r^2\alpha$$

Use $\quad M\bar{x} = \displaystyle\sum_{\theta=-\alpha}^{\theta=\alpha} \tfrac{1}{2}\rho r^2\,\delta\theta \times \tfrac{2}{3}r\cos\theta$

As $\delta\theta \to 0$, the summation becomes an integral

and $\quad M\bar{x} = \displaystyle\int_{-\alpha}^{\alpha} \tfrac{1}{3}\rho r^3\cos\theta\,d\theta = \tfrac{1}{3}\rho r^3\big[\sin\theta\big]_{-\alpha}^{\alpha}$

$$= \tfrac{1}{3}\rho r^3 2\sin\alpha$$

And so $\bar{x} = \dfrac{\tfrac{2}{3}\rho r^3\sin\alpha}{\rho r^2\alpha} = \dfrac{2r\sin\alpha}{3\alpha}$

The distance of the centre of mass from O is $\dfrac{2r\sin\alpha}{3\alpha}$ and it lies on the axis of symmetry. •——

> This is the formula for the area of the sector of a circle formula.

> Point R is the foot of the perpendicular from G onto the x-axis.

> The centre of mass of a triangle lies at the intersection of the mediators at a point $\frac{2}{3}$ along the mediator from the vertex.

> As $\delta\theta$ is small $\cos\left(\theta + \dfrac{\delta\theta}{2}\right) \approx \cos\theta$ and this is a reasonable approximation.

> This formula is included in the formula sheet, but you should understand and learn how to derive it, as in this example.

Example 8

Find the centre of mass of a uniform wire in the form of an arc of a circle, radius r and centre O, which subtends an angle 2α at O.

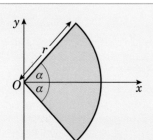 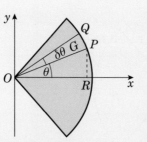

Divide the arc into elements and note that the arc PQ shown has length $r\,\delta\theta$ and mass $\rho r\,\delta\theta$.

This is the formula for arc length given in book C2.

The length OR is $r\cos\theta$.

R is the foot of the perpendicular from P to the x-axis.

The mass M of the whole wire is $\rho \times r2\alpha = 2\rho r\alpha$

Use $M\bar{x} = \displaystyle\sum_{\theta=-\alpha}^{\theta=\alpha} \rho r\,\delta\theta \times r\cos\theta$

As $\delta\theta \to 0$ the summation becomes an integral and

$$M\bar{x} = \int_{-\alpha}^{\alpha} \rho r^2 \cos\theta\,d\theta = \rho r^2 \left[\sin\theta\right]_{-\alpha}^{\alpha} = \rho r^2\, 2\sin\alpha$$

And so $\bar{x} = \dfrac{2\rho r^2 \sin\alpha}{2\rho r\alpha} = \dfrac{r\sin\alpha}{\alpha}$

The centre of mass lies on the axis of symmetry, and is at a distance $\dfrac{r\sin\alpha}{\alpha}$ from O.

This formula appears on the formula sheet and you should be able to use it. You will not be expected to reproduce this proof in your M3 examination.

Exercise 5A

1 Find, by integration, the centre of mass of the uniform triangular lamina enclosed by the lines $y = 6 - 3x$, $x = 0$ and $y = 0$.

2 Use integration to find the centre of mass of the uniform lamina occupying the finite region bounded by the curve with equation $y = 3x^2$, the x-axis and the line $x = 2$.

3 Use integration to find the centre of mass of the uniform lamina occupying the finite region bounded by the curve with equation $y = \sqrt{x}$, the x-axis and the line $x = 4$.

4 Use integration to find the centre of mass of the uniform lamina occupying the finite region bounded by the curve with equation $y = x^3 + 1$, the x-axis and the line $x = 1$.

5 Use integration to find the centre of mass of the uniform lamina occupying the finite region bounded by the curve with equation $y^2 = 4ax$, and the line $x = a$, where a is a positive constant.

6 Find the centre of mass of the uniform lamina occupying the finite region bounded by the curve with equation $y = \sin x$, $(0 \leqslant x \leqslant \pi)$ and the line $y = 0$.

7 Find the centre of mass of the uniform lamina occupying the finite region bounded by the curve with equation $y = \dfrac{1}{1 + x}$ $(0 < x < 1)$ and the lines $x = 0$, $x = 1$ and $y = 0$.

8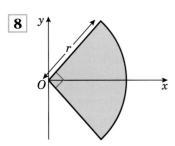

Find, by integration, the centre of mass of a uniform lamina in the shape of a quadrant of a circle of radius r as shown.

9 The figure shows a uniform lamina bounded by the curve $y = x^3$ and the line with equation $y = 4x$, where $x > 0$.
Find the coordinates of the centre of mass of the lamina.

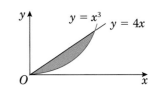

10 The figure shows a badge cut from a uniform sheet of fabric. The badge is formed from one semi-circle of radius 1 cm and a semi-circle of radius 3 cm joined as shown in the figure to make a plane lamina. Both semi-circles have the same centre O. Determine, in terms of pi, the distance from O of the centre of mass.

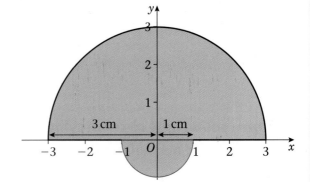

11

The figure shows a uniform lamina made from a sector of a circle with radius 5 cm from which a similar sector of radius 2.5 cm has been removed. The sector is three quarters of the original circle in each case, and both circles have the same centre O.

Find the distance of the centre of mass of the lamina from the point O.

12 The figure shows a uniform lamina occupying the finite region bounded by the x-axis, the curve $y = \sqrt{(24 - 4x)}$, where $2 \leqslant x \leqslant 6$, and the line with equation $y = 2x$, where $0 \leqslant x \leqslant 2$.
Find the coordinates of the centre of mass of the lamina.

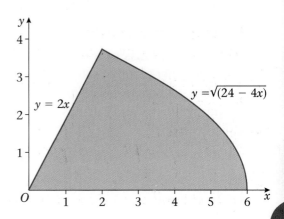

5.2 You can find the centre of mass of a uniform solid of revolution using symmetry and calculus.

■ • For a solid body the centre of mass is the point where the weight acts.

• For a uniform solid body the weight is evenly distributed through the body.

• The centre of mass will lie on any axis of symmetry.

• The centre of mass will lie on any plane of symmetry.

There are certain regular solids whose centre of mass lie at their geometric centre.

Uniform solid sphere

• **The centre of mass of a uniform solid sphere is at the centre of the sphere.**
This point is the intersection of the infinite number of planes of symmetry and is the only point which lies on all of them.

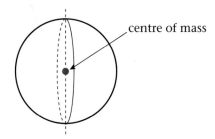

centre of mass

Uniform solid right circular cylinder

• **The centre of mass of a uniform solid right circular cylinder is at the centre of the cylinder.**
This point is the intersection of the axis of symmetry and the plane of symmetry, which bisects the axis and is parallel to the circular ends.

centre of mass

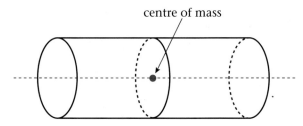

Uniform solid right prism

• **The centre of mass of a uniform right prism is at the centre of the prism.**
There is another group of solids which are formed by rotating a region through 360° about the x-axis. It is possible to calculate the position of the centre of mass of these solids of revolution by using symmetry and calculus.

Example 9

Find the centre of mass of the uniform solid of revolution formed by rotating the finite region enclosed by the curve $y = f(x)$, the x-axis and the line $x = a$ through $360°$ about the x-axis.

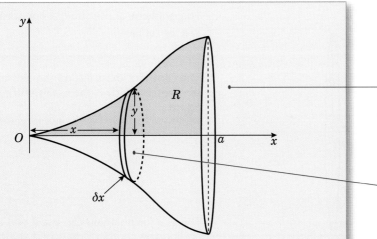

Draw a diagram showing the region R which is rotated about the x-axis to form the solid of revolution.

Show one of these discs on your diagram.

Divide the volume up into a series of very thin circular discs of radius y and thickness δx.

Each disc has volume $\pi y^2 \, \delta x$ and each has centre of mass at a distance x from O.

So if the distance of the centre of mass of the whole solid of revolution from O is $\bar{x}$,

$$\sum \rho \pi y^2 \, \delta x \,.\, \bar{x} = \sum \rho \pi y^2 x \, \delta x, \text{ where } \rho \text{ is the density,}$$

or mass per unit volume.

You now use the formula $\sum m_i x_i = \bar{x} \sum m_i$ applied to this volume.

As $\delta x \to 0$, the number of discs becomes infinite and in the limit the sum is replaced by an integral:

$$\bar{x} = \frac{\int \rho \pi y^2 x \, dx}{\int \rho \pi y^2 \, dx},$$

which may be written

If the rotation were about the y-axis you would use the equivalent formula
$$\bar{y} = \frac{\int \rho \pi x^2 y \, dy}{\int \rho \pi x^2 \, dy}$$

$$\bar{x} = \frac{\int \pi y^2 x \, dx}{\int \pi y^2 \, dx} \text{ or } M\bar{x} = \int \rho \pi y^2 x \, dx, \text{ where } M \text{ is the known}$$

mass of the solid.

■ **For a solid of revolution,** where the revolution is about the x-axis, the centre of mass lies on the x-axis and its position on the axis is given by the formulae

- $\bar{x} = \dfrac{\int \pi y^2 x \, dx}{\int \pi y^2 \, dx}$ or $M\bar{x} = \int \rho \pi y^2 x \, dx$, where M is the known mass of the solid

■ **For a solid of revolution,** where the revolution is about the y-axis, the centre of mass lies on the y-axis and its position on the axis is given by the formulae

- $\bar{y} = \dfrac{\int \pi x^2 y \, dy}{\int \pi x^2 \, dy}$ or $M\bar{y} = \int \rho \pi x^2 y \, dy$, where M is the known mass of the solid

This is obtained from the previous result by interchanging x and y.

Example 10

Find the centre of mass of the uniform solid right circular cone with radius R and height h.

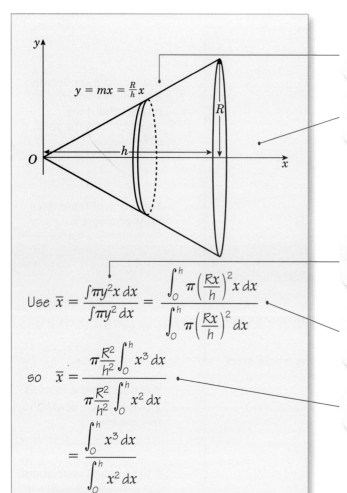

The gradient of the straight line through O is m, where $m = \dfrac{R}{h}$.

The centre of mass lies on the axis of symmetry, which is the x-axis in the figure.

$$\text{Use } \bar{x} = \frac{\int \pi y^2 x\, dx}{\int \pi y^2\, dx} = \frac{\int_0^h \pi \left(\dfrac{Rx}{h}\right)^2 x\, dx}{\int_0^h \pi \left(\dfrac{Rx}{h}\right)^2 dx}$$

This is a formula you can use if you are finding the centre of mass of a volume of revolution.

The cone is generated by the straight line $y = \dfrac{R}{h}x$, which is rotated through 2π radians about the x-axis.

$$\text{so } \bar{x} = \frac{\pi \dfrac{R^2}{h^2} \displaystyle\int_0^h x^3\, dx}{\pi \dfrac{R^2}{h^2} \displaystyle\int_0^h x^2\, dx}$$

This is equivalent to the volume of the cone, i.e. $\tfrac{1}{3}\pi R^2 h$.

$$= \frac{\displaystyle\int_0^h x^3\, dx}{\displaystyle\int_0^h x^2\, dx}$$

$$= \frac{\left[\dfrac{x^4}{4}\right]_0^h}{\left[\dfrac{x^3}{3}\right]_0^h}$$

$$= \frac{\left(\dfrac{h^4}{4}\right)}{\left(\dfrac{h^3}{3}\right)}$$

$$= \frac{3}{4}h$$

■ The centre of mass of a uniform right circular cone lies on the axis of symmetry and is at a distance $\tfrac{3}{4}h$ from the vertex, or $\tfrac{1}{4}h$ from the circular base.

Example 11

Find the centre of mass of the uniform solid hemisphere with radius R.

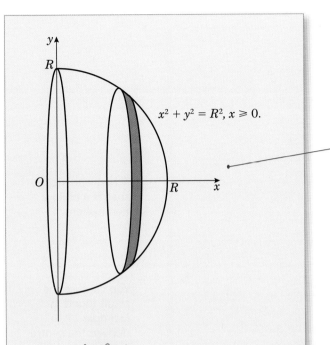

$x^2 + y^2 = R^2, x \geqslant 0.$

> The centre of mass lies on the axis of symmetry, which is the x-axis in the figure.

Use $\bar{x} = \dfrac{\int \pi y^2 x \, dx}{\int \pi y^2 \, dx}$

$= \dfrac{\displaystyle\int_0^R \pi(R^2 - x^2)x \, dx}{\displaystyle\int_0^R \pi(R^2 - x^2) \, dx}$

$= \dfrac{\int R^2 x - x^3 \, dx}{\int R^2 - x^2 \, dx}$

$= \dfrac{\left[R^2 \dfrac{x^2}{2} - \dfrac{x^4}{4} \right]_0^R}{\left[R^2 x - \dfrac{x^3}{3} \right]_0^R}$

$= \dfrac{\left(\dfrac{R^4}{4} \right)}{\left(\dfrac{2R^3}{3} \right)}$

$= \dfrac{3}{8} R$

> Divide the sphere up into a series of circular discs.
> As in Example 9, each disc has volume $\pi y^2 \, \delta x$ and centre of mass at a distance x from O.
> So if the distance of the centre of mass of the sphere from O is $\bar{x}$, then, as $\delta x \to 0$
> $$\bar{x} = \frac{\int \pi y^2 x \, dx}{\int \pi y^2 \, dx}$$

> The sphere is generated by the circle $y^2 = R^2 - x^2$, which is rotated through 2π radians about the x-axis, so replace y^2 by $R^2 - x^2$.

> This is a result which is in the formula book, but you should learn it.

■ The centre of mass of a uniform solid hemisphere lies on the axis of symmetry and is at a distance $\frac{3}{8}R$ from the plane surface.

Example 12

Find the centre of mass of the uniform hemispherical shell with radius R.

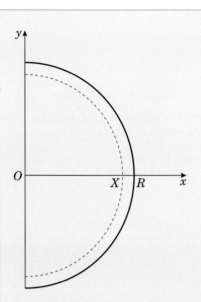

You may obtain a hollow hemisphere by removing a solid concentric hemisphere of radius X from the solid hemisphere of radius R.

Shape	Mass	Centre of mass
Solid hemisphere radius R	$\frac{2}{3}\rho\pi R^3$	$\left(\frac{3}{8}R, 0\right)$
Solid hemisphere radius X	$\frac{2}{3}\rho\pi X^3$	$\left(\frac{3}{8}X, 0\right)$
Hollow shell	$\frac{2}{3}\rho\pi(R^3 - X^3)$	$(\bar{x}, 0)$

Taking moments about a horizontal axis through O in the plane face of the hemisphere,

$$\frac{2}{3}\rho\pi R^3 \times \frac{3}{8}R - \frac{2}{3}\rho\pi X^3 \times \frac{3}{8}X = \frac{2}{3}\rho\pi(R^3 - X^3) \times \bar{x}$$

So $\bar{x} = \dfrac{3}{8} \times \dfrac{R^4 - X^4}{R^3 - X^3} = \dfrac{3}{8} \times \dfrac{(R - X)(R + X)(R^2 + X^2)}{(R - X)(R^2 + RX + X^2)}$

$$= \frac{3}{8}\frac{(R + X)(R^2 + X^2)}{(R^2 + RX + X^2)}$$

As $X \rightarrow R$ you obtain the result for a hemispherical shell.

$$\bar{x} = \frac{3}{8} \times \frac{(2R)(2R^2)}{(3R^2)}$$

$$= \frac{1}{2}R$$

A hemispherical shell is a hollow hemisphere.

You can use the result found in Example 11 to deduce the centre of mass of a hollow sphere.

Draw a table similar to those used in book M2 and in Section 5.1.

From symmetry you can deduce that the centre of mass lies on the x-axis.

This result is included in the formula book. You can also prove it using calculus methods, as you will see in Exercise 5B. You will not be required to prove this result in your M3 examination.

■ The centre of mass of a uniform hemispherical shell lies on the axis of symmetry and is at a distance $\frac{1}{2}R$ from the plane surface.

Example 13

Show that the centre of mass of the uniform hollow right circular cone with radius R and height h is at a distance $\frac{1}{3}h$ from the base along the axis of symmetry.

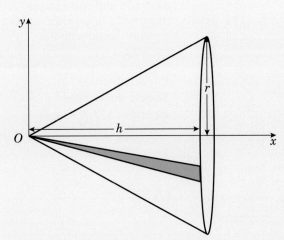

Divide the surface of the cone up into triangular strips with vertices at O and with bases on the circumference of the circular base of the cone. One is shown in the figure.

Each of these triangles has centre of mass $\frac{2}{3}$ of the distance from O to the base of the cone.

So the centre of mass of the hollow cone is also $\frac{2}{3}$ of the distance from O to the base of the cone, but is on the axis of symmetry.

> Use symmetry to obtain this result.

> The distance of the centre of mass from the base is
> $h - \frac{2}{3}h = \frac{1}{3}h$

■ **The centre of mass of a hollow cone lies on the axis of symmetry and is at a distance $\frac{1}{3}h$ from the base.**

Example 14

Find the position of the centre of mass of the frustum of a right circular uniform cone, of end radii 1 cm and 4 cm and of height 7 cm.

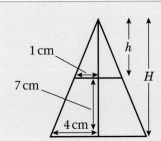

From similar triangles $\frac{h}{H} = \frac{1}{4}$ or $H = 4h$.

But $H = 7 + h$, so $h = \frac{7}{3}$, and $H = \frac{28}{3}$.

> A frustum is a portion of the cone lying between two parallel planes. It may be considered as a large cone with a small cone removed from the top.

> Let the large cone have height H and the small cone have height h.

Shape	Mass	Centre of mass
Large cone	$\frac{1}{3}\rho\pi 4^2 H = \frac{64}{3}\rho\pi h$	$\left(\frac{1}{4}H, 0\right) = \left(\frac{7}{3}, 0\right)$
Small cone	$\frac{1}{3}\rho\pi 1^2 h = \frac{1}{3}\rho\pi h$	$\left(7 + \frac{1}{4}h, 0\right) = \left(\frac{91}{12}, 0\right)$
Frustum	$\frac{63}{3}\rho\pi h = 21\rho\pi h$	$(\bar{x}, 0)$

The masses are in the ratio $64:1:63$ and you can use these ratios in your moments equation to simplify the working.

Taking moments about X,

$$\frac{64}{3}\rho\pi h \times \frac{7}{3} - \frac{1}{3}\rho\pi h \times \frac{91}{12} = 21\rho\pi h\bar{x}$$

So you would have
$$64 \times \frac{7}{3} - 1 \times \frac{91}{12} = 63\bar{x}$$

$$\text{So } \bar{x} = \left(\frac{448}{9} - \frac{91}{36}\right) \div 21 = 2.25$$

The centre of mass is 2.25 cm above the base on the axis of symmetry.

Example 15

A uniform solid right circular cone of height $2R$ and base radius R is joined at its base to the base of a uniform solid hemisphere. The centres of their bases coincide at O and their axes are collinear. The radius of the hemisphere is $2R$.

Find the position of the centre of mass of the composite body if

a the cone and hemisphere are of the same mass per unit volume,

b the cone has four times the mass per unit volume of the hemisphere.

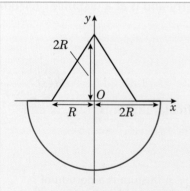

You may choose to measure distances to centres of mass from the base of the hemisphere instead. If you do this you need to remember to add $2R$ to $\frac{1}{4}(2R)$ for the cone.

a Let ρ be the mass per unit volume for each solid.

Shape	Mass	Units of mass	Distance from O to centre of mass
Cone	$\frac{1}{3}\rho\pi R^2(2R)$	1	$\frac{1}{4}(2R) = \dfrac{R}{2}$
Hemisphere	$\frac{2}{3}\rho\pi(2R)^3$	8	$-\frac{3}{8}(2R) = -\dfrac{3R}{4}$
Composite body	$\frac{1}{3}\rho\pi R^2(2R) + \frac{2}{3}\rho\pi(2R)^3$	9	$\bar{x}$

The centre of mass lies on the common axis of symmetry.

Take moments about an axis through O:

$$1 \times \frac{R}{2} - 8 \times \frac{3R}{4} = 9 \times \bar{x}$$

So $\bar{x} = -\frac{11}{18} R$

> You can again use ratios of masses to solve the problem.

b Let ρ be the mass per unit volume for the hemisphere and 4ρ be the mass per unit volume for the cone.

> You may be told that one has **density** equal to four times that of the other.

Shape	Mass	Units of mass	Distance from O to centre of mass
Cone	$\frac{1}{3}4\rho\pi R^2(2R)$	4	$\frac{1}{4}(2R) = \frac{R}{2}$
Hemisphere	$\frac{2}{3}\rho\pi(2R)^3$	8	$-\frac{3}{8}(2R) = -\frac{3R}{4}$
Composite body	$\frac{1}{3}4\rho\pi R^2(2R) + \frac{2}{3}\rho\pi(2R)^3$	12	$\bar{x}$

Again the centre of mass lies on the common axis of symmetry.

Take moments about an axis through O:

$$4 \times \frac{R}{2} - 8 \times \frac{3R}{4} = 12 \times \bar{x}$$

So $\bar{x} = -\frac{4}{12}R = -\frac{1}{3}R$

> Most of the working is the same as in part **a**, but do not forget that the composite body will change mass as well as the cone.

Exercise 5B

In questions 1–4 use symmetry to find the coordinates of the centre of mass of the solid.

1 The finite region bounded by the curve $y = x^2 - 4x$ and the x-axis is rotated through $360°$ about the x-axis to form a solid of revolution. Find the coordinates of its centre of mass.

2 The finite region bounded by the curve $(x - 1)^2 + y^2 = 1$ is rotated through $180°$ about the x-axis to form a solid of revolution. Find the coordinates of its centre of mass.

3 The finite region bounded by the curve $y = \cos x$, $\frac{\pi}{2} \leqslant x \leqslant \frac{3x}{2}$, and the x-axis, is rotated through $360°$ about the x-axis to form a solid of revolution. Find the coordinates of its centre of mass.

4 The finite region bounded by the curve $y^2 + 6y = x$ and the y-axis, is rotated through $360°$ about the y-axis to form a solid of revolution. Find the coordinates of its centre of mass.

In questions 5–10 use integration to find the position of the centre of mass of the solid.

5 Find, by integration, the coordinates of the centre of mass of the solid formed when the finite region bounded by the curve $y = 3x^2$, the line $x = 1$ and the x-axis is rotated through $360°$ about the x-axis.

6 Find, by integration, the coordinates of the centre of mass of the solid formed when the finite region bounded by the curve $y = \sqrt{x}$, the line $x = 4$ and the x-axis is rotated through 360° about the x-axis.

7 Find, by integration, the coordinates of the centre of mass of the solid formed when the finite region bounded by the curve $y = 3x^2 + 1$, the lines $x = 0$, $x = 1$ and the x-axis is rotated through 360° about the x-axis.

8 Find, by integration, the coordinates of the centre of mass of the solid formed when the finite region bounded by the curve $y = \dfrac{3}{x}$, the lines $x = 1$, $x = 3$ and the x-axis is rotated through 360° about the x-axis.

9 Find, by integration, the coordinates of the centre of mass of the solid formed when the finite region bounded by the curve $y = 2e^x$, the lines $x = 0$, $x = 1$ and the x-axis is rotated through 360° about the x-axis.

10 Find, by integration, the coordinates of the centre of mass of the solid formed when the finite region bounded by the curve $y = 3e^{-x}$, the lines $x = 0$, $x = 2$ and the x-axis is rotated through 360° about the x-axis.

In questions 11–16 you may quote results for the centres of mass of cones and hemispheres obtained earlier.

11 A uniform solid right circular cone of height 10 cm and base radius 5 cm is joined at its base to the base of a uniform solid hemisphere. The centres of their bases coincide and their axes are collinear. The radius of the hemisphere is also 5 cm. Find the position of the centre of mass of the composite body,

  a when both the cone and the hemisphere have the same density,

  b when the hemisphere has density twice that of the cone.

12 A solid is composed of a uniform solid right circular cylinder of height 10 cm and base radius 6 cm joined at its top plane face to the base of a uniform hemisphere of the same radius. The centres of their adjoining circular faces coincide at point O and their axes are collinear. The radius of the hemisphere is also 6 cm. Find the position of the centre of mass of the composite body,

  a if the cylinder and hemisphere are of the same density,

  b if the hemisphere has three times the density of the cylinder.

13 Find the position of the centre of mass of the frustum of a right circular uniform solid cone, where the frustum has end radii 2 cm and 5 cm, and has height 4 cm.

14 a Find the position of the centre of mass of the frustum of a right circular uniform solid cone, where the frustum has end radii 2 cm and 4 cm, and has height 8 cm.

b A cylindrical hole of radius 1 cm with the same axis as that of the frustum is now drilled through the frustum. Find the distance of the new centre of mass from the larger face of the frustum.

15 A thin uniform hemispherical shell has a circular base of the same material. Find the position of the centre of mass above the base in terms of its radius r.

16 A thin uniform hollow cone has a circular base of the same material. Find the position of the centre of mass above the base, given that the radius of the cone is 3 cm and its height is 4 cm.

In questions 17–19 use calculus to obtain your answer.

17 A cap of height 3 cm is cut from a uniform solid sphere of radius 6 cm. Using calculus, find the position of the centre of mass of the cap, giving the distance from the plane circular surface.

18 Show that the centre of mass of a cap of height h of a sphere of radius a is on its axis of symmetry at a distance $\dfrac{h(4a - h)}{4(3a - h)}$ from the circular base of the cap.

19 Using calculus, find the centre of mass of the uniform hemispherical shell with radius R.

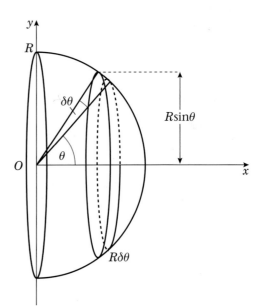

Hint: Divide the shell into small elemental cylindrical rings, centred on the x-axis, with radius $R \sin \theta$, and height $R \, \delta\theta$, where θ is the angle between the radius R and the x-axis.

5.3 You can solve problems about rigid bodies which are in equilibrium.

In book M2 you used the fact that if a body is resting in equilibrium then there is zero resultant force in any direction. This means that the sum of the components of all the forces in any direction is zero, and the sum of the moments of the forces about any point is zero.

In M2 you applied this fact to problems where the body was modelled as a uniform rod, e.g. ladder problems.

In this section you will use the same principle to solve problems involving rigid bodies in equilibrium, where the body may be modelled as a simple solid of revolution or as a composite body made up of these solids.

Suspension of a body from a fixed point

■ When a lamina is suspended freely from a fixed point or pivots freely about a horizontal axis it will rest in equilibrium in a vertical plane with its centre of mass vertically below the point of suspension or pivot.

> This was in Section 2.6 of book M2.

This result is also true for a rigid body.

Let the body be suspended from a point A. The body rests in equilibrium and the only forces acting on the body are its weight and the force at point A. This implies that the forces must be equal and opposite and act in the same vertical line.

■ When a rigid body is suspended freely from a fixed point and rests in equilibrium then its centre of mass is vertically below the point of suspension.

Example 16

A uniform solid hemisphere has radius r. It is suspended by a string attached to a point A on the rim of its base. Find the angle between the axis of the hemisphere and the downward vertical when the hemisphere is in equilibrium.

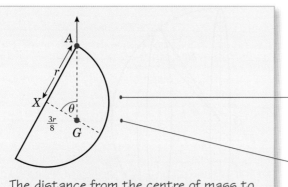

Draw a diagram showing the centre of mass, G, of the hemisphere below the point of suspension A.

Mark the angle between GA and the axis of the hemisphere and mark the radius and length XG.

The distance from the centre of mass to the base is $\dfrac{3r}{8}$ so $XG = \dfrac{3r}{8}$.

Let $\angle XGA$ be θ.

Use trigonometry to solve the problem.

Then $\tan \theta = \dfrac{r}{\frac{3}{8}r} = \dfrac{8}{3}$.

So the required angle is $69.4°$.

Equilibrium of bodies resting on a plane surface

■ If a lamina rests in equilibrium on a rough inclined plane, then the line of action of the weight of the lamina must pass through the side of the lamina AB which is in contact with the plane.

> This was in Section 2.6 of book M2.

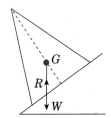

A similar result applies for a rigid body.

The only forces acting on the body are its weight and the total reaction between the plane and the body. As the body is in equilibrium, these forces must be equal and opposite and act in the same vertical line.

■ **When a rigid body rests in equilibrium on a horizontal or rough inclined plane, then the line of action of the weight of the body must pass through the area of contact with the plane.**

Example 17

A uniform solid right cone is of height 8 cm and base radius 4 cm. A frustum is cut from the cone by a plane parallel to the base at a height 4 cm from the base.

a Show that the centre of mass of the frustum is at a height $\frac{11}{7}$ cm from the base along the axis of symmetry.

b Show that the frustum rests in equilibrium when it is placed with its curved surface in contact with the horizontal plane.

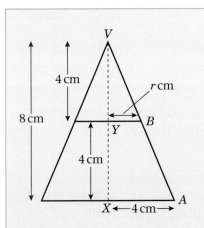

Let the small cone have base radius r cm, and height 4 cm (by subtraction). Mark lengths of sides and points V, A, X, Y, and B on your figure.

a From similar triangles $\frac{r}{4} = \frac{4}{8}$ so $r = 2$.

Shape	Mass	Ratios of masses	Height of centre of mass above base in cm
Large cone	$\frac{1}{3}\rho\pi 4^2 \times 8 = \frac{128}{3}\rho\pi$	8	2
Small cone	$\frac{1}{3}\rho\pi 2^2 \times 4 = \frac{16}{3}\rho\pi$	1	$4 + 1 = 5$
Frustum	$\frac{112}{3}\rho\pi$	7	$\bar{x}$

The height of the centre of mass of a solid cone above its base, is $\frac{h}{4} = \frac{8}{4} = 2$ cm.

This is $\frac{4}{4} = 1$ cm above base of small cone, i.e. $1 + 4 = 5$ cm above base of large cone.

So $8 \times 2 - 1 \times 5 = 7\bar{x}$

$\bar{x} = \frac{11}{7}$

Now take moments to find the position of the centre of mass of the frustum.

139

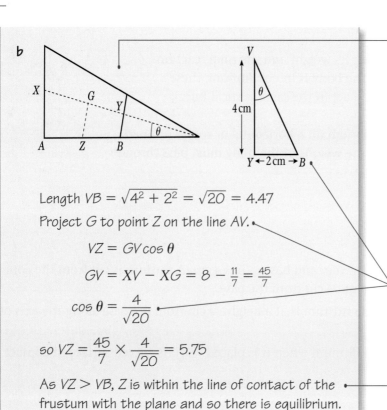

b

Draw a figure to show the cone resting on its curved surface. Indicate points V, B, A, X and Y. Also show G the centre of mass of the frustum, and θ the angle between VB and the axis VY.

Length $VB = \sqrt{4^2 + 2^2} = \sqrt{20} = 4.47$

Project G to point Z on the line AV.

$$VZ = GV\cos\theta$$

$$GV = XV - XG = 8 - \tfrac{11}{7} = \tfrac{45}{7}$$

$$\cos\theta = \frac{4}{\sqrt{20}}$$

Also draw triangle VYB and calculate VB using Pythagoras, (i.e. $\sqrt{20}$) and $\cos\theta$ using trigonometry.

$$\text{so } VZ = \frac{45}{7} \times \frac{4}{\sqrt{20}} = 5.75$$

As $VZ > VB$, Z is within the line of contact of the frustum with the plane and so there is equilibrium.

Point Z is between A and B.

Example 18

A solid uniform cylinder of base radius 3 cm and height 5 cm has a solid uniform hemisphere made from the same material, of base radius 3 cm, joined to it so that the base of the hemisphere coincides with one circular end of the cylinder.

a Find the position of the centre of mass of the composite body.

The composite body is placed with the circular face of the cylinder on a rough inclined plane, which is inclined at an angle α to the horizontal. Given that the plane is sufficiently rough to prevent sliding,

b show that equilibrium is maintained provided that $\tan\alpha < \frac{28}{33}$.

a

Shape	Mass	Ratios of masses	Height of centre of mass above base in cm
Cylinder	$\rho\pi 3^2 \times 5 = 45\rho\pi$	5	2.5
Hemisphere	$\frac{2}{3}\rho\pi 3^3 = 18\rho\pi$	2	$5 + \frac{3}{8} \times 3 = 6.125$
Composite body	$63\rho\pi$	7	$\bar{x}$

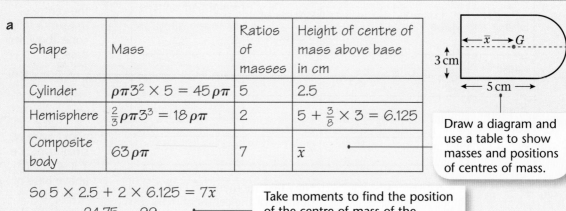

Draw a diagram and use a table to show masses and positions of centres of mass.

So $5 \times 2.5 + 2 \times 6.125 = 7\bar{x}$

and $\bar{x} = \dfrac{24.75}{7} = \dfrac{99}{28}$.

Take moments to find the position of the centre of mass of the composite body.

b From the figure $\tan \alpha = \dfrac{3}{\frac{99}{28}} = 3 \times \dfrac{28}{99} = \dfrac{28}{33}$.

If α is smaller than this value, G is above a point of contact and equilibrium is maintained. Equilibrium is maintained provided that $\tan \alpha < \dfrac{28}{33}$.

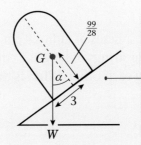

The limiting case is shown in the figure, where the point vertically below the centre of mass, G, is on the edge of the area of contact.

> If $\tan \alpha > \dfrac{28}{33}$ then the body will topple over because there will be a turning effect about the point A.

Further problems concerning rigid bodies in equilibrium

Example 19

The figure shows a uniform solid right cone, of mass M with radius r and height $3r$. P and Q are points at opposite ends of a diameter on the circular plane face of the cone. The cone is suspended from a horizontal beam by two vertical inelastic strings fastened at P and Q. Given that the cone is in equilibrium with its axis at an angle of $45°$ to the horizontal, find the values of the tensions in the strings, giving your answers in terms of M and g.

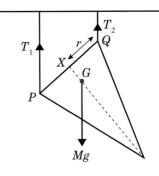

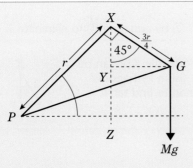

Let the tensions in the strings be T_1 and T_2.

Resolve vertically:

$$T_1 + T_2 = Mg \qquad \text{①}$$

Take moments about point P:

$$T_2 \times 2r\cos 45 = Mg\left(r\cos 45 + \frac{3r}{4}\sin 45\right) \qquad \text{②}$$

Divide equation ② through by $2r\cos 45$, then $T_2 = \frac{7}{8}mg$

Substitute into equation ① to give $T_1 = \frac{1}{8}mg$.

So the tensions are $\frac{1}{8}mg$ and $\frac{7}{8}mg$.

> Moments could be taken about a number of points, but choosing point P eliminates T_1 and simplifies the algebra.

> The distance PW is $PZ + ZW$. Also $ZW = YG$. So from the diagram
> $$PW = r\cos 45 + \frac{3r}{4}\sin 45.$$

Example 20

Two smooth uniform spheres of radius 4 cm and mass 5 kg are suspended from the same point A by light inextensible strings of length 8 cm attached to their surfaces. The spheres hang in equilibrium, touching each other. What is the reaction between them?

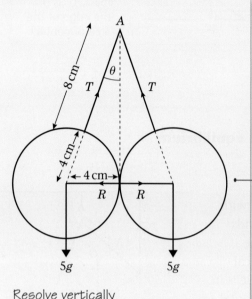

From symmetry, the tensions in the two strings are equal.

Resolve vertically

$T\cos\theta = 5g$ ①

Resolve horizontally

$T\sin\theta = R$ ②

Eliminating T gives $R = 5g\tan\theta$.

Divide equation ② by equation ① to eliminate T.

From the geometry of the figure

$\sin\theta = \frac{4}{12} = \frac{1}{3}$ and so $\tan\theta = \frac{1}{2\sqrt{2}}$.

So $R = \dfrac{5g}{2\sqrt{2}} = 17$ (2 s.f.).

As $\sin\theta = \frac{1}{3}$ the triangle XYZ can be used to find XY using Pythagoras' theorem, and then to find $\tan\theta$.

$XY^2 = 3^2 - 1^2$ $\quad\therefore XY = \sqrt{8} = 2\sqrt{2}$.

Exercise 5C

1 A uniform solid right circular cone is suspended by a string attached to a point on the rim of its base. Given that the radius of the base is 5 cm and the height of the cone is 8 cm, find the angle between the vertical and the axis of the cone when it is in equilibrium.

2 A uniform solid right circular cylinder is suspended by a string attached to a point on the rim of its base. Given that the radius of the base is 6 cm and the height of the cylinder is 10 cm, find the angle between the vertical and the circular base of the cylinder when it is in equilibrium.

3 A uniform hemispherical shell is suspended by a string attached to a point on the rim of its base. Given that the radius of the base is 4 cm, find the angle between the vertical and the axis of the hemisphere when it is in equilibrium.

4 **a** Find the position of the centre of mass of the frustum of a right circular uniform solid cone, of end radii 4 cm and 5 cm and of height 6 cm. (Give your answer to 3 s.f.)

This frustum is now suspended by a string attached to a point on the rim of its smaller circular face.

b Find the angle between the vertical and the axis of the frustum when it is in equilibrium. (Give your answer to the nearest degree.)

5 A uniform solid cylinder of radius r and height $4r$ rests in equilibrium with its base in contact with a rough inclined plane, which is sufficiently rough to prevent sliding. The plane is inclined at an angle α to the horizontal. Show that equilibrium is maintained provided that $\tan \alpha \leqslant k$ and find the value of k.

6 A uniform hollow cone of radius r and height $4r$ rests in equilibrium with its base in contact with a rough inclined plane, which is sufficiently rough to prevent sliding. The plane is inclined at an angle α to the horizontal. Show that equilibrium is maintained provided that $\tan \alpha \leqslant k$ and find the value of k.

7 A uniform solid hemisphere of radius r rests in equilibrium with its curved surface in contact with a rough inclined plane, which is sufficiently rough to prevent sliding. The plane is inclined at an angle α to the horizontal, and the plane face of the hemisphere is in a vertical position. Find the value of α, giving your answer to the nearest degree.

8 A solid uniform hemisphere rests in equilibrium with its curved surface in contact with a rough plane inclined at α to the horizontal where $\sin \alpha = \frac{3}{16}$.

Find the inclination of the axis of symmetry of the hemisphere to the vertical.

9 A solid object is made up of a right circular uniform solid cone joined to a uniform solid hemisphere so that the base of the cone coincides with the plane surface of the hemisphere. Their common radius is r and the height of the cone is $\frac{2}{3}r$.

a Find the position of the centre of mass of the composite object giving the distance of this centre of mass from the vertex of the cone.

b Show that the object will remain in equilibrium on a smooth horizontal plane, if it is placed with a curved surface of the cone in contact with the plane.

10 A uniform solid consists of a hemisphere of radius r and a right circular uniform cylinder of base radius r and height h fixed together so that their circular faces coincide. The solid can rest in equilibrium with any point of the curved surface of the hemisphere in contact with a horizontal plane. Find h in terms of r.

11 You may assume that the centre of mass of a uniform semi-circular lamina of radius a is at a distance $\frac{4a}{3\pi}$ from the centre.

A uniform solid right circular cylinder is cut in half through its axis to form two prisms of semi-circular cross section. One of these is placed with its curved surface in contact with a rough inclined plane as shown in the figure. The inclined plane makes an angle of 20° with the horizontal. Show that when the prism is in equilibrium, its rectangular plane face makes an angle α with the horizontal, where α is approximately 54°.

12 A hemispherical bowl, which may be modelled as a uniform hemispherical shell, has mass 3 kg. A weight of 2 kg is placed on the rim and the bowl rests in equilibrium on a smooth horizontal plane. The plane surface of the bowl makes an angle α with the horizontal. Show that $\tan \alpha = \frac{4}{3}$.

13 A uniform solid right circular cone has base radius r, height $4r$ and mass m. One end of a light inextensible string is attached to the vertex of the cone and the other end is attached to a point on the rim of the base. The string passes over a smooth peg and the cone rests in equilibrium with the axis horizontal, and with the strings equally inclined to the horizontal at an angle θ, as shown in the figure.

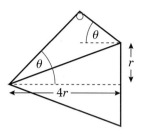

a Show that angle θ satisfies the equation $\tan \theta = \frac{1}{2}$.

b Find the tension in the string, giving your answer as an exact multiple of mg.

5.4 You can determine whether a body will remain in equilibrium or whether equilibrium will be broken by sliding or toppling.

Example **21**

A uniform solid cube of mass M and side $2a$ rests on a rough horizontal plane. The coefficient of friction is μ. A horizontal force of magnitude P is applied at the mid-point of an upper edge, perpendicular to that edge, as shown in the figure. The reaction between the plane and the cube is comprised of a normal reaction force R and a friction force F and acts at a distance h from a lower edge of the cube as shown in the figure.

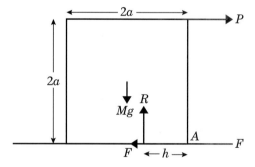

Find whether the cube remains in equilibrium, or whether the equilibrium is broken by sliding or toppling, in each of the following cases. Also determine the value of F and the value of h in each case, giving your answers in terms of M, g and a as appropriate:

a $P = 0$ **b** $P = \frac{1}{2}Mg$ and $\mu = \frac{3}{4}$ **c** $P = \frac{1}{4}Mg$ and $\mu = \frac{1}{5}$.

For equilibrium	First use the conditions for equilibrium in the general case. i.e. Resolve horizontally, resolve vertically and take moments.
Resolve horizontally →	
$\quad P - F = 0$, so $F = P$ ①	
Resolve vertically ↑	
$\quad R - Mg = 0$ so $R = Mg$ ②	
Take moments about point A.	A is the point on the bottom edge of the cube shown in the figure.
$\quad P \times 2a + R \times h = Mg \times a$ ③	

a When $P = 0$

Substituting result from equation ② into equation ③:

$$0 + Mgh = Mga$$
$$h = a$$

> For part **a** substitute $P = 0$ in equations ①, ② and ③.

> In part **a** the normal reaction acts at the centre of the base.

Substituting $P = 0$ into equation ① gives $F = 0$.

The cube remains in equilibrium – it does not slip and does not topple.

b When $P = \frac{1}{2}Mg$

Substituting result from equation ② into equation ③:

$$\frac{1}{2}Mg \times 2a + Mgh = Mga$$

$h = 0$, and the cube is about to topple.

Substituting $P = \frac{1}{2}Mg$ into equation ① gives $F = \frac{1}{2}Mg$.

But $\mu R = \frac{3}{4}Mg$ so $F < \mu R$ and the body does not slip.

> For part **b** substitute $P = \frac{1}{2}mg$ in equations ①, ② and ③.

> In part **b** the normal reaction acts at A and so toppling is about to occur around the edge through A.

c When $P = \frac{1}{4}Mg$

Substituting result from equation ② into equation ③:

$$\frac{1}{4}Mg \times 2a + Mgh = Mga$$

$h = \frac{1}{2}a$, and the cube does not topple.

Substituting $P = \frac{1}{4}Mg$ into equation ① would give $F = \frac{1}{4}Mg$.

But this is impossible as the maximum value that F can take is μR and $\mu R = \frac{1}{5}Mg$ so $F = \frac{1}{5}Mg$.

The cube will accelerate if the force P is maintained.

> This implies that the body does not topple as the reaction is within the area of the base.

> Assuming equilibrium leads to a contradiction. This cube will slip as the force P exceeds the maximum friction force.

■ **A body is on the point of sliding when $F = \mu R$.**

■ **A body is on the point of toppling when the reaction acts at the point about which turning can take place.**

Example 22

A uniform solid cube of mass M and side $2a$, is placed on a rough inclined plane which is at an angle α to the horizontal, where $\tan \alpha = \frac{1}{2}$. The coefficient of friction is μ.

Show that if $\mu < \frac{1}{2}$ the cube will slip down the slope.

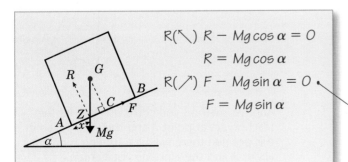

$$R(\nwarrow)\ R - Mg\cos\alpha = 0$$
$$R = Mg\cos\alpha$$
$$R(\nearrow)\ F - Mg\sin\alpha = 0$$
$$F = Mg\sin\alpha$$

> Draw a diagram showing G the centre of mass of the cube, and points A and B on the edges of the cube in the same vertical plane as G.

> First use the conditions for equilibrium. i.e. Resolve along and perpendicular to the plane and use $F \leqslant \mu R$, where F is the force of friction and R is the normal reaction.

For equilibrium $F \leqslant \mu R$, i.e. $\mu \geqslant \dfrac{F}{R}$

So $\mu \geqslant \dfrac{Mg \sin \alpha}{Mg \cos \alpha}$

i.e. $\mu \geqslant \tan \alpha$ and so $\mu \geqslant \frac{1}{2}$ for equilibrium.

So if $\mu < \frac{1}{2}$ the cube will slide.

Let the point Z, vertically below the centre of mass G, be at a distance x from A up the plane.

Let C be the mid-point of AB.

From triangle GCZ, $\dfrac{a-x}{a} = \tan \alpha = \dfrac{1}{2}$

So $2a - 2x = a$

$x = \frac{1}{2}a$

So Z is between A and B and the cube does not topple.

As $\tan \alpha = \frac{1}{2}$, the limiting case is when $\mu = \frac{1}{2}$.

Draw an enlarged triangle if it helps.

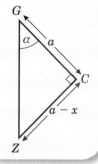

The normal reaction would act at point Z, which could also be established by taking moments and using the equilibrium conditions.

So the weight of the cube acts through a point within the area of contact.

Example 23

The cube in the previous example is now replaced by a cylinder of mass M with base radius a and height $6a$. The cylinder is placed on the rough inclined plane, which is inclined at an angle α to the horizontal, where $\tan \alpha = \frac{1}{2}$. The coefficient of friction is μ. Show that if $\mu > \frac{1}{2}$ the cylinder will topple about the lower edge.

As $\mu > \frac{1}{2}$ the cylinder will not slip.

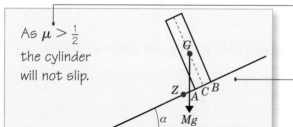

Let the point Z, vertically below the centre of mass G, be at a distance x from A down the plane.

Let C be the mid-point of AB.

From triangle GCZ, $\dfrac{a+x}{3a} = \tan \alpha = \dfrac{1}{2}$

So $2a + 2x = 3a$

$x = \frac{1}{2}a$

So Z is not between A and B and the cylinder will topple.

This condition was shown in Example 22, and the working here would be identical. i.e. Resolve along and perpendicular to the plane and use $F \leqslant \mu R$.

The points A, B, C, G and Z are defined as in Example 22.

Draw an enlarged triangle GZC.

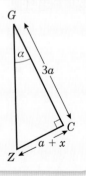

Another method you could use is to let the reaction act at point A and show that even in this position there will be a turning moment about A and therefore no equilibrium.

Example 24

A uniform solid cone of mass M, height 8 cm and radius 3 cm, rests on a horizontal plane. The coefficient of friction is μ. A horizontal force of magnitude P is applied at the vertex of the cone.

a Find the value of P which will cause the cone to slide giving your answer in terms of μ, M and g.

b Find the value of P which will cause the cone to tilt, giving your answer in terms of M and g.

c State whether the cone will slide or tilt if **i** $\mu = \frac{1}{4}$, **ii** $\mu = \frac{1}{2}$, **iii** $\mu = \frac{3}{8}$.

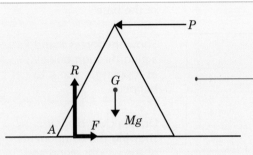

Draw a diagram showing the forces acting and let A be the point on the circumference of the base of the cone about which tilting would occur. G is the position of the centre of mass and R and F are the normal reaction and the frictional forces.

a Resolve horizontally $F - P = 0$,
$$F = P$$
Resolve vertically $R - Mg = 0$,
$$R = Mg$$
Limiting equilibrium is when $F = \mu R$
i.e. when $P = \mu Mg$
So the cone will slip when $P > \mu Mg$

You find the condition for slipping by letting $F = \mu R$.

When tilting is about to happen R acts at point A, as the cone will turn about point A.

b Let R act at the point marked A.
Take moments about A:
$$P \times 8 = Mg \times 3$$
$$P = \frac{3}{8} Mg$$
So the cone will tilt when $P > \frac{3}{8} Mg$

R and F both pass through point A so have zero moment about A.

c **i** When $\mu = \frac{1}{4}$, the cone will slip when P exceeds $\frac{1}{4} Mg$.

ii When $\mu = \frac{1}{2}$, the cone will tilt when P exceeds $\frac{3}{8} Mg$.

iii When $\mu = \frac{3}{8}$, the cone will slip and tilt when P exceeds $\frac{3}{8} Mg$.

As P reaches $\frac{1}{4} Mg$ before it reaches $\frac{3}{8} Mg$.

P will not reach $\frac{1}{2} Mg$, the condition for sliding.

Both conditions are reached at the same time.

Example 25

A uniform solid cylinder of mass 200 g, height 4 cm and radius 3 cm rests on a plane which makes an angle α with the horizontal where $\tan \alpha = \frac{3}{4}$. The coefficient of friction is $\frac{6}{17}$. A horizontal force P is applied to the highest point of the cylinder.

a Find the value of P which will just cause the cylinder to topple about the highest point of the base.

b Find the value of P which would cause the cylinder to slide up the plane.

c Show that the cylinder topples before it slides.

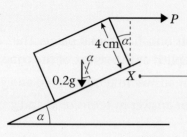

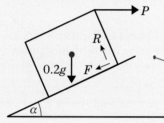

You can draw a 3, 4, 5 triangle to show that
$\tan \alpha = \frac{3}{4}$ implies
$\sin \alpha = \frac{3}{5}$ and
$\cos \alpha = \frac{4}{5}$.

Let X be the highest point of the base.

Show the forces R and F acting through point X, as toppling is about to happen.

Draw a clear diagram showing the components of the weight along and perpendicular to the plane.

a

Take moments about X:

$P \times 4\cos \alpha = 0.2g\cos \alpha \times 3 + 0.2g\sin \alpha \times 2$

So $P = \dfrac{9g}{40}$ or $2.2\,\text{N}$ (2 s.f.) is the force which will just cause the cylinder to topple.

R and F have zero moment about X, which simplifies the moments equation.

Using resolved components of the weight simplifies the moments equation.

b

The friction force acts down the plane, as the cylinder is about to slip up the plane.

Resolve perpendicular to plane:

$R - 0.2g\cos \alpha - P\sin \alpha = 0$

So $R = 0.2g\cos \alpha + P\sin \alpha$

Resolve along the plane

$F + 0.2g\sin \alpha - P\cos \alpha = 0$

So $F = P\cos \alpha - 0.2g\sin \alpha$

For limiting equilibrium $F = \frac{6}{17}R$.

First use the conditions for equilibrium.
i.e. Resolve along and perpendicular to the plane.

You find the condition for slipping by letting $F = \mu R$.

$P\cos \alpha - 0.2g\sin \alpha = \frac{6}{17}(0.2g\cos \alpha + P\sin \alpha)$

$P(\cos \alpha - \frac{6}{17}\sin \alpha) = 0.2g(\frac{6}{17}\cos \alpha + \sin \alpha)$

$\frac{10}{17}P = \frac{3}{17}g$

Substitute $\sin \alpha = \frac{3}{5}$ and $\cos \alpha = \frac{4}{5}$ to find P.

$P = \dfrac{3g}{10} = 2.9\,\text{N}$ (2 s.f.) is the force which will just cause the cylinder to slide up the plane.

c As $2.2 < 2.9$ the cylinder will topple before it slides.

Compare the two critical values of P to determine which is reached first.

Exercise 5D

1 A uniform solid right circular cylinder with base diameter 4 cm stands on a rough plane inclined at 40° to the horizontal. What is the maximum height that such a cylinder can have without toppling over?

2 A uniform solid right circular cylinder with base radius 3 cm and height 10 cm is placed with its circular plane base on a rough plane. The plane is gradually tilted.

   a Find the angle which the plane makes with the horizontal if the cylinder topples over before it slides.

   b What can you deduce about the value of the coefficient of friction?

3 A uniform solid right circular cone with base radius 5 cm and height h cm is placed with its circular plane base on a rough plane. The coefficient of friction is $\frac{\sqrt{3}}{3}$. The plane is gradually tilted.

   a Find the angle which the plane makes with the horizontal if the cone is about to slide and topple at the same time.

   b Calculate the value of the height of the cone, h cm.

4 A uniform solid right circular cone of mass M with base radius r and height $2r$ is placed with its circular plane base on a rough horizontal plane. A force P is applied to the vertex V of the cone at an angle of 60° above the horizontal as shown in the figure.

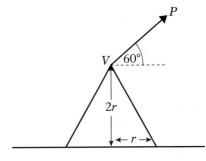

   The cone begins to topple and to slide at the same time.

   a Find the magnitude of the force P in terms of M.

   b Calculate the value of the coefficient of friction.

5 A frustum of a right circular solid cone has two plane circular end faces with radii r and $2r$ respectively. The distance between the end faces is $2r$.

   a Show that the centre of mass of the frustum is at a distance $\frac{11r}{14}$ from the larger circular face.

   b Find whether this solid can rest without toppling on a rough plane, inclined to the horizontal at an angle of 40°, if the face in contact with the inclined plane is
     i the large circular end,   **ii** the small circular end.

   c In order to answer part **b** you assumed that slipping did not occur. What does this imply about the coefficient of friction μ?

6 A uniform cube with edges of length $6a$ and weight W stands on a rough horizontal plane. The coefficient of friction is μ. A gradually increasing force P is applied at right angles to a vertical face of the cube at a point which is a distance a above the centre of that face.

   a Show that equilibrium will be broken by sliding or toppling depending on whether $\mu < \frac{3}{4}$ or $\mu > \frac{3}{4}$.

   b If $\mu = \frac{1}{4}$, and the cube is about to slip, find the distance from the point where the normal reaction acts, to the nearest vertical face of the cube.

7 A spindle is formed by joining two solid right circular cones so that their circular bases coincide. The cones have the same base radius and have the same uniform density. The heights of the two cones are h and $2h$ as shown in the figure.

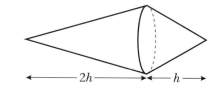

a Find the distance of the centre of mass of the spindle from the vertex of the larger cone.

The spindle is placed on horizontal ground with the sloping surface of the smaller cone in contact with the ground. It rests in equilibrium but is on the point of toppling.

b Show that the radius of the common base of the two cones is $\frac{1}{2}h$.   **E**

8 A uniform solid cylinder of base radius r and height h has the same density as a uniform solid hemisphere of radius r. The plane face of the hemisphere is joined to a plane face of the cylinder to form the composite solid S shown. The point O is the centre of the plane base of S.

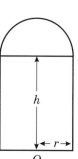

a Show that the distance from O to the centre of mass of S is $\dfrac{6h^2 + 8hr + 3r^2}{4(3h + 2r)}$.

The solid is placed on a rough plane which is inclined at an angle α to the horizontal. The plane base of S is in contact with the inclined plane.

b Given that $h = 3r$ and that S is on the point of toppling, find α to the nearest degree.

c Given that the solid did not slip before it toppled, find the range of possible values for the coefficient of friction.   **E** [adapted]

9 A uniform solid paperweight is in the shape of a frustum of a cone. It is formed by removing a right circular cone of height h from a right circular cone of height $2h$ and base radius $2r$.

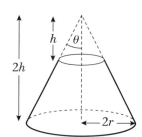

a Show that the centre of mass of the paperweight lies at a height of $\frac{11}{28}h$ from its base.

When placed with its curved surface on a horizontal plane, the paperweight is on the point of toppling.

b Find θ, the semi-vertical angle of the cone, to the nearest degree.   **E**

10 A child's toy is made from joining a right circular uniform solid cone, radius r and height h, to a uniform solid hemisphere of the same material and radius r. They are joined so that their plane faces coincide as shown in the figure.

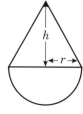

a Show that the distance of the centre of mass of the toy from the base of the cone is

$$\left| \frac{h^2 - 3r^2}{4(2r + h)} \right|.$$

The toy is placed with its hemisphere in contact with a horizontal plane and with its axis vertical. It is slightly displaced and released from rest.

b Given that the plane is sufficiently rough to prevent slipping, explain clearly, with reasons, what will happen in each of the following cases:

i $h > r\sqrt{3}$ **ii** $h < r\sqrt{3}$ **iii** $h = r\sqrt{3}$.   **E**

Mixed exercise 5E

1 The curve shows a sketch of the region R bounded by the curve with equation $y^2 = 4x$ and the line with equation $x = 4$. The unit of length on both the axes is the centimetre. The region R is rotated through π radians about the x-axis to form a solid S.

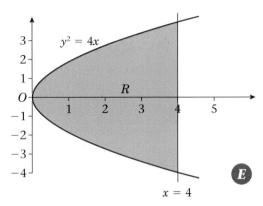

a Show that the volume of the solid S is $32\pi\,\text{cm}^3$.

b Given that the solid is uniform, find the distance of the centre of mass of S from O.

E

2

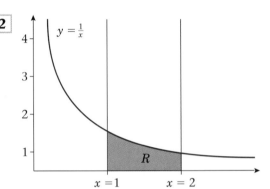

The region R is bounded by the curve with equation $y = \dfrac{1}{x}$, the lines $x = 1$, $x = 2$ and the x-axis, as shown in the figure. The unit of length on both the axes is $1\,\text{m}$. A solid plinth is made by rotating R through 2π radians about the x-axis.

a Show that the volume of the plinth is $\dfrac{\pi}{2}\,\text{m}^3$.

b Find the distance of the centre of mass of the plinth from its larger plane face, giving your answer in cm to the nearest cm.

E

3 The figure shows a uniform solid standing on horizontal ground. The solid consists of a uniform solid right circular cylinder, of diameter $80\,\text{cm}$ and height $40\,\text{cm}$, joined to a uniform solid hemisphere of the same density. The circular base of the hemisphere coincides with the upper circular end of the cylinder and has the same diameter as that of the cylinder. Find the distance of the centre of mass of the solid from the ground.

E

4 A simple wooden model of a rocket is made by taking a uniform cylinder, of radius r and height $3r$, and carving away part of the top two thirds to form a uniform cone of height $2r$ as shown in the figure. Find the distance of the centre of mass of the model from its plane face.

E

5 The figure shows a cross section containing the axis of symmetry of a uniform body consisting of a solid right circular cylinder of base radius r and height kr surmounted by a solid hemisphere of radius r. Given that the centre of mass of the body is at the centre C of the common face of the cylinder and the hemisphere, find the value of k, giving your answer to 2 significant figures.

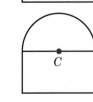

Explain briefly why the body remains at rest when it is placed with any part of its hemispherical surface in contact with a horizontal plane.

E

6 A uniform lamina occupies the region R bounded by the x-axis and the curve with equation $y = \frac{1}{4}x(4 - x)$ $0 \leqslant x \leqslant 4$, as shown in Figure 1.

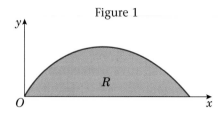

Figure 1

a Show by integration that the y-coordinate of the centre of mass of the lamina is $\frac{2}{5}$.

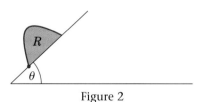

Figure 2

A uniform prism P has cross section R. The prism is placed with its rectangular face on a slope inclined at an angle θ to the horizontal. The cross section R lies in a vertical plane as shown in Figure 2. The surfaces are sufficiently rough to prevent P from sliding.

b Find the angle θ, for which P is about to topple.

7 A uniform semi-circular lamina has radius $2a$ and the mid-point of the bounding diameter AB is O.

a Using integration, show that the centre of mass of the lamina is at a distance $\frac{8a}{3\pi}$ from O.

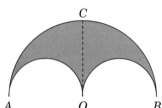

The two semi-circular laminas, each of radius a and with AO and OB as diameters, are cut away from the original lamina to leave the lamina $AOBC$ shown in the diagram, where OC is perpendicular to AB.

b Show that the centre of mass of the lamina $AOBC$ is at a distance $\frac{4a}{\pi}$ from O.

The lamina $AOBC$ is of mass M and a particle of mass M is attached to the lamina at B to form a composite body.

c State the distance of the centre of mass of the body from OC and from OB.

The body is smoothly hinged at A to a fixed point and rests in equilibrium in a vertical plane.

d Calculate, to the nearest degree, the acute angle between AB and the horizontal. **E**

8 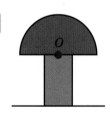 A uniform wooden 'mushroom', used in a game, is made by joining a solid cylinder to a solid hemisphere. They are joined symmetrically, such that the centre O of the plane face of the hemisphere coincides with the centre of one of the ends of the cylinder. The diagram shows the cross section through a plane of symmetry of the mushroom, as it stands on a horizontal table.

The radius of the cylinder is r, the radius of the hemisphere is $3r$, and the centre of mass of the mushroom is at the point O.

a Show that the height of the cylinder is $r\sqrt{\frac{81}{2}}$.

The table top, which is rough enough to prevent the mushroom from sliding, is slowly tilted until the mushroom is about to topple.

b Find, to the nearest degree, the angle with the horizontal through which the table top has been tilted. **E**

9 Figure 1 shows a finite region A which is bounded by the curve with equation $y^2 = 4ax$, the line $x = a$ and the x-axis.

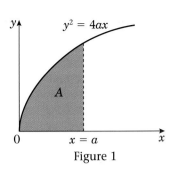

Figure 1

A uniform solid S_1 is formed by rotating A through 2π radians about the x-axis.

a Show that the volume of S_1 is $2\pi a^3$.

b Show that the centre of mass of S_1 is a distance $\dfrac{2a}{3}$ from the origin O.

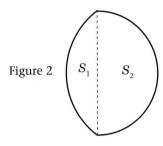

Figure 2

Figure 2 shows a cross section of a uniform solid S which has been obtained by attaching the plane base of solid S_1 to the plane base of a uniform hemisphere S_2 of base radius $2a$.

c Given that the densities of solids S_1 and S_2 are ρ_1 and ρ_2 respectively, find the ratio $\rho_1 : \rho_2$ which ensures that the centre of mass of S lies in the common plane face of S_1 and S_2.

d Given that $\rho_1 : \rho_2 = 6$, explain why the solid S may rest in equilibrium with any point of the curved surface of the hemisphere in contact with a horizontal plane. **E**

10 A mould for a right circular cone, base radius r and height h, is produced by making a conical hole in a uniform cylindrical block, base radius $2r$ and height $3r$. The axis of symmetry of the conical hole coincides with that of the cylinder, and AB is a diameter of the top of the cylinder, as shown in the figure.

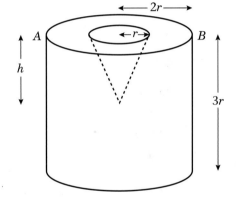

a Show that the distance from AB of the centre of mass of the mould is

$$\frac{216r^2 - h^2}{4(36r - h)}$$

The mould is suspended from the point A, and hangs freely in equilibrium.

b In the case $h = 2r$, calculate, to the nearest degree, the angle between AB and the downward vertical. **E**

Summary of key points

1 The centre of mass of a lamina may be found using the formulae

- $\bar{x} = \dfrac{\displaystyle\int_a^b xy\,\mathrm{d}x}{\displaystyle\int_a^b y\,\mathrm{d}x}$ and $\bar{y} = \dfrac{\displaystyle\int_a^b \tfrac{1}{2}y^2\,\mathrm{d}x}{\displaystyle\int_a^b y\,\mathrm{d}x}$

- $M\bar{x} = \displaystyle\int_a^b \rho xy\,\mathrm{d}x$ and $M\bar{y} = \displaystyle\int_a^b \tfrac{1}{2}\rho y^2\,\mathrm{d}x$,

  where $M = \displaystyle\int_a^b \rho y\,\mathrm{d}x$, and is the total mass of the lamina.

2 Standard results for uniform lamina and for arcs

Lamina	Centre of mass along axis of symmetry
Semi-circle, radius r	$\dfrac{4r}{3\pi}$ from the centre
Sector of circle, radius r, angle at centre 2α	$\dfrac{2r\sin\alpha}{3\alpha}$ from the centre
Circular arc, radius r, angle at centre 2α	$\dfrac{r\sin\alpha}{\alpha}$ from the centre

3 • For a solid body the centre of mass is the point where the weight acts.
  • For a uniform solid body the weight is evenly distributed through the body.
  • The centre of mass will lie on any axis of symmetry.
  • The centre of mass will lie on any plane of symmetry.

4 For a solid of revolution, where the revolution is about the x-axis, the centre of mass lies on the x-axis, by symmetry, and its position on the axis is given by the formulae

$$\bar{x} = \frac{\int \pi y^2 x \, dx}{\int \pi y^2 \, dx} \text{ or } M\bar{x} = \int \rho\pi y^2 x \, dx, \text{ where } M \text{ is the known mass of the solid}$$

5 For a solid of revolution, where the revolution is about the y-axis, the centre of mass lies on the y-axis, by symmetry, and its position on the axis is given by the formulae

$$\bar{y} = \frac{\int \pi x^2 y \, dy}{\int \pi x^2 \, dy} \text{ or } M\bar{y} = \int \rho\pi x^2 y \, dy, \text{ where } M \text{ is the known mass of the solid}$$

6 From symmetry, the centre of mass of some uniform bodies is at their geometric centre. These include the cube, the cuboid, the sphere, the right circular cylinder and the right circular prism.

7 Standard results for uniform bodies.

Body	Centre of mass along axis of symmetry
Solid hemisphere, radius R	$\frac{3}{8}R$ from the centre
Hemispherical shell, radius R	$\frac{1}{2}R$ from the centre
Solid right circular cone, height h	$\frac{3}{4}h$ from the vertex, or $\frac{1}{4}h$ from the circular base
Conical shell, height h	$\frac{2}{3}h$ from the vertex, or $\frac{1}{3}h$ from the circular base

8 A rigid body is in equilibrium if
  • there is zero resultant force in any direction, i.e. the sum of the components of all the forces in any direction is zero.
  • the sum of the moments of the forces about any point is zero.

9 • **When a rigid body is suspended freely** from a fixed point and rests in equilibrium its centre of mass is vertically below the point of suspension.
  • **When a rigid body rests in equilibrium on a horizontal or rough inclined plane**, then the line of action of the weight of the body must pass through the area of contact with the plane.

10 You can establish whether equilibrium will be broken by sliding or by toppling by considering
  • a body is on the point of sliding when $F = \mu R$,
  • a body is on the point of toppling when the reaction acts at the point about which turning can take place.

Review Exercise

1 A circular flywheel of diameter 7 cm is rotating about the axis through its centre and perpendicular to its plane with constant angular speed 1000 revolutions per minute.

Find, in m s⁻¹ to 3 significant figures, the speed of a point on the rim of the flywheel. **E**

2

A particle P of mass m is attached to one end of a light string. The other end of the string is attached to a fixed point A. The particle moves in a horizontal circle with constant angular speed ω and with the string inclined at an angle of 60° to the vertical, as shown in the diagram above. The length of the string is L.

a Show that the tension in the string is $2mg$.

b Find ω in terms of g and L. **E**

3 A car moves round a bend which is banked at a constant angle of 10° to the horizontal. When the car is travelling at a constant speed of $18\,\mathrm{m\,s^{-1}}$, there is no sideways frictional force on the car. The car is modelled as a particle moving in a horizontal circle of radius r metres. Calculate the value of r. **E**

4 A cyclist is travelling around a circular track which is banked at 25° to the horizontal. The coefficient of friction between the cycle's tyres and the track is 0.6. The cyclist moves with constant speed in a horizontal circle of radius 40 m, without the tyres slipping.

Find the maximum speed of the cyclist. **E**

5

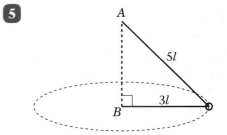

A light inextensible string of length $8l$ has its ends fixed to two points A and B, where

A is vertically above B. A small smooth ring of mass m is threaded on the string. The ring is moving with constant speed in a horizontal circle with centre B and radius $3l$, as shown in the diagram. Find

a the tension in the string,

b the speed of the ring.

c State briefly in what way your solutions might no longer be valid if the ring were firmly attached to the string.

6

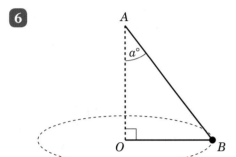

A metal ball B of mass m is attached to one end of a light inextensible string. The other end of the string is attached to a fixed point A. The ball B moves in a horizontal circle with centre O vertically below A, as shown in the diagram. The string makes a constant angle $\alpha°$ with the downward vertical and B moves with constant angular speed $\sqrt{(2gk)}$, where k is a constant. The tension in the string is $3mg$. By modelling B as a particle, find

a the value of α,

b the length of the string. **E**

7 A particle P of mass 0.5 kg is attached to one end of a light inextensible string of length 1.5 m. The other end of the string is attached to a fixed point A. The particle is moving, with the string taut, in a horizontal circle with centre O vertically below A. The particle is moving with constant angular speed 2.7 rad s^{-1}. Find

a the tension in the string,

b the angle, to the nearest degree, that AP makes with the downward vertical. **E**

8 A particle P of mass m moves on the smooth inner surface of a spherical bowl of internal radius r. The particle moves with constant angular speed in a horizontal circle, which is at a depth $\frac{1}{2}r$ below the centre of the bowl.

a Find the normal reaction of the bowl on P.

b Find the time for P to complete one revolution of its circular path. **E**

9

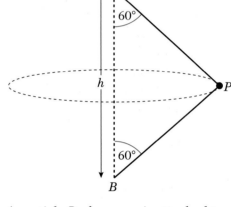

A particle P of mass m is attached to two light inextensible strings. The other ends of the string are attached to fixed points A and B. The point A is a distance h vertically above B. The system rotates about the line AB with constant angular speed ω. Both strings are taut and inclined at 60° to AB, as shown in the diagram. The particle moves in a circle of radius r.

a Show that $r = \frac{\sqrt{3}}{2}h$.

b Find, in terms of m, g, h and ω, the tension in AP and the tension in BP.

The time taken for P to complete one circle is T.

c Show that $T < \pi\sqrt{\left(\frac{2h}{g}\right)}$. **E**

10

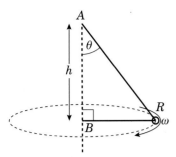

One end of a light inextensible string is attached to a fixed point A. The other end of the string is attached to a fixed point B, vertically below A, where $AB = h$. A small smooth ring R of mass m is threaded on the string. The ring R moves in a horizontal circle with centre B, as shown in the diagram. The upper section of the string makes a constant angle θ with the downward vertical and R moves with constant angular speed ω. The ring is modelled as a particle.

a Show that $\omega^2 = \dfrac{g}{h}\left(\dfrac{1 + \sin\theta}{\sin\theta}\right)$.

b Deduce that $\omega > \sqrt{\dfrac{2g}{h}}$.

Given that $\omega = \sqrt{\dfrac{3g}{h}}$,

c find, in terms of m and g, the tension in the string. **E**

11

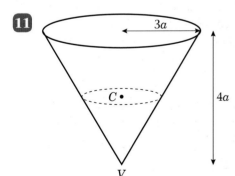

A hollow cone, of base radius $3a$ and height $4a$, is fixed with its axis vertical and vertex V downwards, as shown in the diagram. A particle moves in a horizontal circle with centre C, on the smooth inner surface of the cone with constant angular speed $\sqrt{\dfrac{8g}{9a}}$.

Find the height of C above V.

12

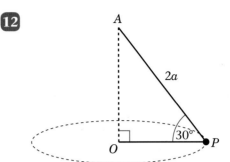

A particle P of mass m is attached to one end of a light inextensible string of length $2a$. The other end of the string is fixed to a point A which is vertically above the point O on a smooth horizontal table. The particle P remains in contact with the surface of the table and moves in a circle with centre O and with angular speed $\sqrt{\dfrac{kg}{3a}}$, where k is a constant. Throughout the motion the string remains taut and $\angle APO = 30°$, as shown in the diagram.

a Show that the tension in the string is $\dfrac{2kmg}{3}$.

b Find, in terms of m, g and k, the normal reaction between P and the table.

c Deduce the range of possible values of k.

The angular speed of P is changed to $\sqrt{\left(\dfrac{2g}{a}\right)}$. The particle P now moves in a horizontal circle above the table. The centre of this circle is X.

d Show that X is the mid-point of OA.

13

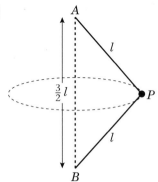

A particle P of mass m is attached to the ends of two light inextensible strings AP and BP each of length l. The ends A and B are attached to fixed points, with A vertically above B and $AB = \frac{3}{2}l$, as shown in the diagram above. The particle P moves in a horizontal circle with constant angular speed ω. The centre of the circle is the mid-point of AB and both strings remain taut.

a Show that the tension in AP is $\frac{1}{6}m(3l\omega^2 + 4g)$.

b Find, in terms of m, l, ω and g, an expression for the tension in BP.

c Deduce that $\omega^2 \geqslant \dfrac{4g}{3l}$. **E**

14 A rough disc rotates in a horizontal plane with constant angular velocity ω about a fixed vertical axis. A particle P of mass m lies on the disc at a distance $\frac{4}{3}a$ from the axis. The coefficient of friction between P and the disc is $\frac{3}{5}$. Given that P remains at rest relative to the disc,

a prove that $\omega^2 \leqslant \dfrac{9g}{20a}$.

The particle is now connected to the axis by a horizontal light elastic string of natural length a and modulus of elasticity $2mg$. The disc again rotates with constant angular velocity ω about the axis and P remains at rest relative to the disc at a distance $\frac{4}{3}a$ from the axis.

b Find the greatest and least possible values of ω^2. **E**

15 One end of a light inextensible string of length l is attached to a particle P of mass m. The other end is attached to a fixed point A. The particle is hanging freely at rest with the string vertical when it is projected horizontally with speed $\sqrt{\dfrac{5gl}{2}}$.

a Find the speed of P when the string is horizontal.

When the string is horizontal it comes into contact with a small smooth fixed peg which is at the point B, where AB is horizontal, and $AB < l$. Given that the particle then describes a complete semi-circle with centre B,

b find the least possible value of the length AB. **E**

16 One end of a light inextensible string of length l is attached to a fixed point A. The other end is attached to a particle P of mass m which is hanging freely at rest at point B. The particle P is projected horizontally from B with speed $\sqrt{3gl}$. When AP makes an angle θ with the downward vertical and the string remains taut, the tension in the string is T.

a Show that $T = mg(1 + 3\cos\theta)$.

b Find the speed of P at the instant when the string becomes slack.

c Find the maximum height above the level of B reached by P. **E**

17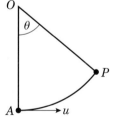

A particle of mass m is attached to one end of a light inextensible string of length l. The other end of the string is attached to a fixed point O. The particle is hanging at the point A, which is vertically below O. It is projected horizontally with speed u. When the particle is at the point P, $\angle AOP = \theta$, as shown in the diagram. The string oscillates through an angle α on either side of OA where $\cos \alpha = \frac{2}{3}$.

a Find u in terms of g and l.

When $\angle AOP = \theta$, the tension in the string is T.

b Show that $T = \dfrac{mg}{3}(9 \cos \theta - 4)$.

c Find the range of values of T.   **E**

18

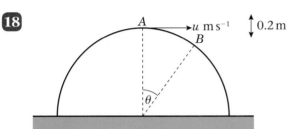

A smooth solid hemisphere, of radius 0.8 m and centre O, is fixed with its plane face on a horizontal table. A particle of mass 0.5 kg is projected horizontally with speed $u\,\mathrm{m\,s^{-1}}$ from the highest point A of the hemisphere. The particle leaves the hemisphere at the point B, which is a vertical distance of 0.2 m below the level of A. The speed of the particle at B is $v\,\mathrm{m\,s^{-1}}$ and the angle between OA and OB is θ, as shown in the diagram.

a Find the value of $\cos \theta$.

b Show that $v^2 = 5.88$.

c Find the value of u.   **E**

19 A smooth solid sphere, with centre O and radius a, is fixed to the upper surface of a horizontal table. A particle P is placed on the surface of the sphere at a point A, where OA makes an angle α with the upper vertical, and $0 < \alpha < \frac{\pi}{2}$. The particle is released from rest. When OP makes an angle θ with the upward vertical, and P is still on the surface of the sphere, the speed of P is v.

a Show that $v^2 = 2ga(\cos \alpha - \cos \theta)$.

Given that $\cos \alpha = \frac{3}{4}$, find

b the value of θ when P loses contact with the sphere,

c the speed of P as it hits the table.   **E**

20

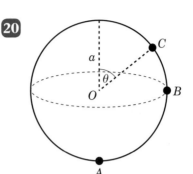

The diagram shows a fixed hollow sphere of internal radius a and centre O. A particle P of mass m is projected horizontally from the lowest point A of the sphere with speed $\sqrt{\left(\frac{7}{2}ag\right)}$. It moves in a vertical circle, centre O, on the smooth inner surface of the sphere. The particle passes through the point B, which is in the same horizontal plane as O. It leaves the surface of the sphere at the point C, where OC makes an angle θ with the upward vertical.

a Find, in terms of m and g, the normal reaction between P and the surface of the sphere at B.

b Show that $\theta = 60°$.

After leaving the surface of the sphere, P meets it again at the point A.

c Find, in terms of a and g, the time P takes to travel from C to A.   **E**

21

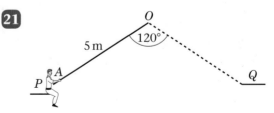

A trapeze artiste of mass 60 kg is attached to the end A of a light inextensible rope

OA of length 5 m. The artiste must swing in an arc of a vertical circle, centre *O*, from a platform *P* to another platform *Q*, where *PQ* is horizontal. The other end of the rope is attached to the fixed point *O* which lies in the vertical plane containing *PQ*, with ∠*POQ* = 120° and *OP* = *OQ* = 5 m, as shown in the diagram.

As part of her act, the artiste projects herself from *P* with speed $\sqrt{15}$ m s^{-1} in a direction perpendicular to the rope *OA* and in the plane *POQ*. She moves in a circular arc towards *Q*. At the lowest point of her path she catches a ball of mass *m* kg which is travelling towards her with speed 3 m s^{-1} and parallel to *QP*. After catching the ball, she comes to rest at the point *Q*.

By modelling the artiste and the ball as particles and ignoring her air resistance, find

a the speed of the artiste immediately before she catches the ball,

b the value of *m*,

c the tension in the rope immediately after she catches the ball. **E**

22

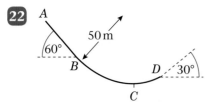

The diagram represents the path of a skier of mass 70 kg moving on a ski-slope *ABCD*. The path lies in a vertical plane. From *A* to *B*, the path is modelled as a straight line inclined at 60° to the horizontal. From *B* to *D*, the path is modelled as an arc of a vertical circle of radius 50 m. The lowest point of the arc *BD* is *C*.

At *B*, the skier is moving downwards with speed 20 m s^{-1}. At *D*, the path is inclined at 30° to the horizontal and the skier is moving upwards. By modelling the slope as smooth and the skier as a particle, find

a the speed of the skier at *C*,

b the normal reaction of the slope on the skier at *C*,

c the speed of the skier at *D*,

d the change in the normal reaction of the slope on the skier as she passes *B*.

The model is refined to allow for the influence of friction on the motion of the skier.

e State briefly, with a reason, how the answer to part **b** would be affected by using such a model. (No further calculations are expected.) **E**

23

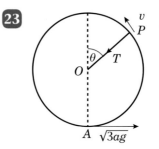

A particle *P* of mass *m* is attached to one end of a light inextensible string of length *a*. The other end of the string is attached to a point *O*. The point *A* is vertically below *O*, and *OA* = *a*. The particle is projected horizontally from *A* with speed $\sqrt{(3ag)}$. When *OP* makes an angle θ with the upward vertical through *O* and the string is still taut, the tension in the string is *T* and the speed of *P* is *v*, as shown in the diagram.

a Find, in terms of *a*, *g* and θ, an expression for v^2.

b Show that $T = (1 - 3\cos\theta)mg$.

The string becomes slack when *P* is at the point *B*.

c Find, in terms of *a*, the vertical height of *B* above *A*.

After the string becomes slack, the highest point reached by *P* is *C*.

d Find, in terms of *a*, the vertical height of *C* above *B*. **E**

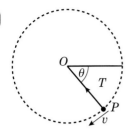

A particle P of mass m is attached to one end of a light inextensible string of length a. The other end of the string is fixed at a point O. The particle is held with the string taut and OP horizontal. It is then projected vertically downwards with speed u, where $u^2 = \frac{3}{2}ga$. When OP has turned through an angle θ and the string is still taut, the speed of P is v and the tension in the string is T, as shown in the diagram above.

a Find an expression for v^2 in terms of a, g and θ.

b Find an expression for T in terms of m, g and θ.

c Prove that the string becomes slack when $\theta = 210°$.

d State, with a reason, whether P would complete a vertical circle if the string were replaced by a light rod.

After the string becomes slack, P moves freely under gravity and is at the same level as O when it is at the point A.

e Explain briefly why the speed of P at A is $\sqrt{\left(\frac{3}{2}ga\right)}$.

The direction of motion of P at A makes an angle ϕ with the horizontal.

f Find ϕ. **E**

25

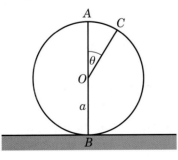

A particle is at the highest point A on the outer surface of a fixed smooth sphere of radius a and centre O. The lowest point B of the sphere is fixed to a horizontal plane. The particle is projected horizontally from A with speed u, where $u < \sqrt{(ag)}$. The particle leaves the sphere at the point C, where OC makes an angle θ with the upward vertical, as shown in the diagram above.

a Find an expression for $\cos\theta$ in terms of u, g and a.

The particle strikes the plane with speed $\sqrt{\left(\frac{9ag}{2}\right)}$.

b Find, to the nearest degree, the value of θ. **E**

26

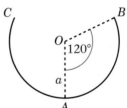

Part of a hollow spherical shell, centre O and radius a, is removed to form a bowl with a plane circular rim. The bowl is fixed with the circular rim uppermost and horizontal. The point A is the lowest point of the bowl. The point B is on the rim of the bowl and $\angle AOB = 120°$, as shown in the diagram above. A smooth small marble of mass m is placed inside the bowl at A and given an initial horizontal speed u. The direction of motion of the marble lies in the vertical plane AOB. The marble stays in contact with the bowl until it reaches B. When the marble reaches B, its speed is v.

a Find an expression for v^2.

b For the case when $u^2 = 6ga$, find the normal reaction of the bowl on the marble as the marble reaches B.

c Find the least possible value of u for the marble to reach B.

The point C is the other point on the rim of the bowl lying in the vertical plane OAB.

d Find the value of u which will enable the marble to leave the bowl at B and meet it again at the point C. **(E)**

27 A uniform solid is formed by rotating the region enclosed between the curve with equation $y = \sqrt{x}$, the x-axis and the line $x = 4$, through one complete revolution about the x-axis. Find the distance of the centre of mass of the solid from the origin O. **(E)**

28

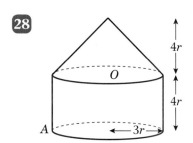

A toy is formed by joining a uniform solid right circular cone, of base radius $3r$ and height $4r$, to a uniform solid cylinder, also of radius $3r$ and height $4r$. The cone and the cylinder are made from the same material, and the plane face of the cone coincides with a plane face of the cylinder, as shown in the diagram. The centre of this plane face is O.

a Find the distance of the centre of mass of the toy from O.

The point A lies on the edge of the plane face of the cylinder which forms the base of the toy. The toy is suspended from A and hangs in equilibrium.

b Find, in degrees to one decimal place, the angle between the axis of symmetry of the toy and the vertical.

The toy is placed with the curved surface of the cone on horizontal ground.

c Determine whether the toy will topple. **(E)**

29

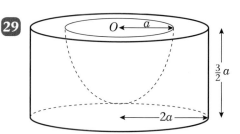

A uniform solid cylinder has radius $2a$ and height $\frac{3}{2}a$. A hemisphere of radius a is removed from the cylinder. The plane face of the hemisphere coincides with the upper plane face of the cylinder, and the centre O of the hemisphere is also the centre of this plane face, as shown in the diagram above. The remaining solid is S.

a Find the distance of the centre of mass of S from O.

The lower plane face of S rests in equilibrium on a desk lid which is inclined at an angle θ to the horizontal. Assuming that the lid is sufficiently rough to prevent S from slipping, and that S is on the point of toppling when $\theta = \alpha$,

b find the value of α.

Given instead that the coefficient of friction between S and the lid is 0.8, and that S is on the point of sliding down the lid when $\theta = \beta$,

c find the value of β.

30

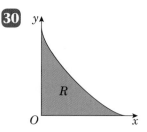

The shaded region R is bounded by part of the curve with equation $y = \frac{1}{2}(x - 2)^2$, the x-axis and the y-axis, as shown above. The unit of length on both axes is 1 cm. A uniform solid S is made by rotating R through $360°$ about the x-axis. Using integration,

a calculate the volume of the solid S, leaving your answer in terms of π,

b show that the centre of mass of S is $\frac{1}{3}$ cm from its plane face.

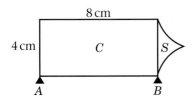

A tool is modelled as having two components, a solid uniform cylinder C and the solid S. The diameter of C is 4 cm and the length of C is 8 cm. One end of C coincides with the plane face of S. The components are made of different materials. The weight of C is $10W$ newtons and the weight of S is $2W$ newtons. The tool lies in equilibrium with its axis of symmetry horizontal on two smooth supports A and B, which are at the ends of the cylinder, as shown above.

c Find the magnitude of the force of the support A on the tool. **E**

31

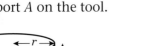

A child's toy consists of a uniform solid hemisphere attached to a uniform solid cylinder. The plane face of the hemisphere coincides with the plane face of the cylinder, as shown in the diagram above. The cylinder and the hemisphere each have radius r and the height of the cylinder is h. The material of the hemisphere is six times as dense as the material of the cylinder. The toy rests in equilibrium on a horizontal plane with the cylinder above the hemisphere and the axis of the cylinder vertical.

a Show that the distance d of the centre of mass of the toy from its lowest point O is given by

$$d = \frac{h^2 + 2hr + 5r^2}{2(h + 4r)}$$

When the toy is placed with any point of the curved surface of the hemisphere resting on the plane it will remain in equilibrium.

b Find h in terms of r. **E**

32

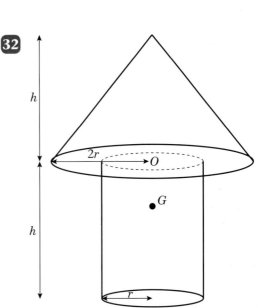

A model tree is made by joining a uniform solid cylinder to a uniform solid cone made of the same material. The centre O of the base of the cone is also the centre of one end of the cylinder, as shown in the diagram. The radius of the cylinder is r and the radius of the base of the cone is $2r$. The height of the cone and the height of the cylinder are each h. The centre of mass of the model is at the point G.

a Show that $OG = \frac{1}{14}h$.

The model stands on a desk top with its plane face in contact with the desk top. The desk top is tilted until it makes an angle α with the horizontal, where $\tan \alpha = \frac{7}{26}$. The desk top is rough enough to prevent slipping and the model is about to topple.

b Find r in terms of h. **E**

33

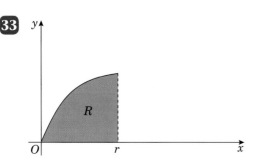

The diagram shows the region R bounded by the curve with equation $y^2 = rx$, where r is a positive constant, the x-axis and the line $x = r$. A uniform solid of revolution S is formed by rotating R through one complete revolution about the x-axis.

a Show that the distance of the centre of mass of S from O is $\frac{2}{3}r$.

The solid is placed with its plane face on a plane which is inclined at an angle α to the horizontal. The plane is sufficiently rough to prevent S from sliding. Given that S does not topple,

b find, to the nearest degree, the maximum value of α. **E**

34

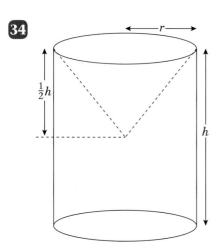

An ornament S is formed by removing a solid right circular cone, of radius r and height $\frac{1}{2}h$, from a solid uniform cylinder, of radius r and height h, as shown in the diagram.

a Show that the distance of the centre of mass of S from its plane face is $\frac{17}{40}h$.

The ornament is suspended from a point on the circular rim of its open end. It hangs in equilibrium with its axis of symmetry inclined at an angle α to the horizontal. Given that $h = 4r$,

b find, in degrees to one decimal place, the value of α. **E**

35

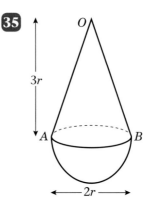

A child's toy consists of a uniform solid hemisphere, of mass M and base radius r, joined to a uniform solid right circular cone of mass m, where $2m < M$. The cone has vertex O, base radius r and height $3r$. Its plane face, with diameter AB, coincides with the plane face of the hemisphere, as shown in the diagram above.

a Show that the distance of the centre of mass of the toy from AB is

$$\frac{3(M - 2m)}{8(M + m)}r.$$

The toy is placed with OA on a horizontal surface. The toy is released from rest and does not remain in equilibrium.

b Show that $M > 26m$. **E**

36 Use integration to show that the centre of mass of a uniform semi-circular lamina, of radius a, is a distance $\frac{4a}{3\pi}$ from the mid-point of its straight edge, O. A semi-circular lamina, of radius b with O as the mid-point of its straight edge, is removed from the first lamina. Show that the centre of mass of the resulting lamina is at a distance $\bar{x}$ from O, where

$$\bar{x} = \frac{4}{3\pi} \frac{(a^2 + ab + b^2)}{(a + b)}$$

Hence find the position of the centre of mass of a uniform semi-circular arc of radius a. **(E)**

---

37 A uniform triangular lamina ABC has $\angle ABC = 90°$ and $AB = c$. Using integration show that the centre of mass of the lamina is at a distance $\frac{1}{3}c$ from BC.

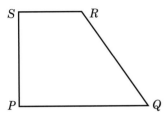

The diagram shows a uniform lamina in which $PQ = PS = 2a$, $SR = a$.

The centre of mass of the lamina is G.

a Show that the distance of G from PS is $\frac{7}{9}a$.

b Find the distance of G from PQ. **(E)**

---

38 A uniform triangular lamina XYZ has $XY = XZ$ and the perpendicular distance of X from YZ is h. Prove, by integration, that the centre of mass of the lamina is at a distance $\frac{2h}{3}$ from X.

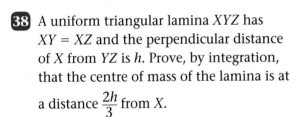

A uniform triangular lamina ABC has $AB = AC = 5a$, $BC = 8a$ and D is the centre of mass of the lamina. The triangle BCD is removed from the lamina, leaving the plate $ABDC$ shown in the diagram.

a Show that the distance of the centre of mass of the plate from A is $\frac{5a}{3}$.

The plate, which is of mass M, has a particle of mass M attached at B. The loaded plate is suspended from C and hangs in equilibrium.

b Prove that in this position CB makes an angle of $\arctan\frac{1}{9}$ with the vertical. **(E)**

39

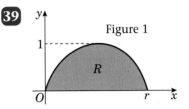

Figure 1

A uniform lamina occupies the region R bounded by the x-axis and the curve $y = \sin x$, $0 \leq x \leq \pi$, as shown in Figure 1.

a Show, by integration, that the y-coordinate of the centre of mass of the lamina is $\frac{\pi}{8}$.

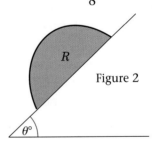

Figure 2

A uniform prism S has cross section R. The prism is placed with its rectangular face on a table which is inclined at an angle θ to the horizontal. The cross section R lies in a vertical plane as shown in Figure 2. The table is sufficiently rough to prevent S sliding. Given that S does not topple,

b find the largest possible value of θ. **(E)**

---

40 A closed container C consists of a thin uniform hollow hemispherical bowl of radius a, together with a lid. The lid is a thin uniform circular disc, also of radius a. The centre O of the disc coincides with the centre of the hemispherical bowl. The bowl and its lid are made of the same material.

a Show that the centre of mass of C is at a distance $\frac{1}{3}a$ from O.

The container C has mass M. A particle of mass $\frac{1}{2}M$ is attached to the container at a point P on the circumference of the lid. The container is then placed with a point of its curved surface in contact with a horizontal plane. The container rests in equilibrium with P, O and the point of contact in the same vertical plane.

b Find, to the nearest degree, the angle made by the line PO with the horizontal. **E**

41

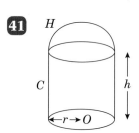

A body consists of a uniform solid circular cylinder C, together with a uniform solid hemisphere H which is attached to C. The plane face of H coincides with the upper plane face of C, as shown in the diagram. The cylinder C has base radius r, height h and mass 3M. The mass of H is 2M. The point O is the centre of the base of C.

a Show that the distance of the centre of mass of the body from O is

$$\frac{14h + 3r}{20}$$

The body is placed with its plane face on a rough plane which is inclined at an angle α to the horizontal, where $\tan \alpha = \frac{4}{3}$. The plane is sufficiently rough to prevent slipping. Given that the body is on the point of toppling,

b find h in terms of r. **E**

42 A bowl consists of a uniform solid metal hemisphere, of radius a and centre O, from which is removed the solid hemisphere of radius $\frac{1}{2}a$ with the same centre O.

a Show that the distance of the centre of mass of the bowl from O is $\frac{45}{112}a$.

The bowl is fixed with its plane face uppermost and horizontal. It is now filled with liquid. The mass of the bowl is M and the mass of the liquid is kM, where k is a constant. Given that the distance of the centre of mass of the bowl and liquid together from O is $\frac{17}{48}a$,

b find the value of k. **E**

43

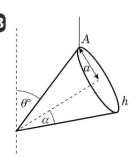

A uniform solid right circular cone has base radius a and semi-vertical angle α, where $\tan \alpha = \frac{1}{3}$. The cone is freely suspended by a string attached at a point A on the rim of its base, and hangs in equilibrium with its axis of symmetry making an angle of $\theta°$ with the upward vertical, as shown in the diagram. Find, to one decimal place, the value of θ. **E**

44

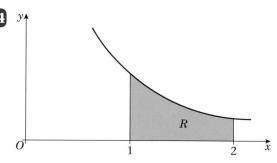

The shaded region R is bounded by the curve with equation $y = \dfrac{1}{2x^2}$, the x-axis and the lines $x = 1$ and $x = 2$, as shown above. The unit of length on each axis is 1 m. A uniform solid S has the shape made by rotating R through 360° about the x-axis.

a Show that the centre of mass of S is $\frac{2}{7}$ m from its larger plane face.

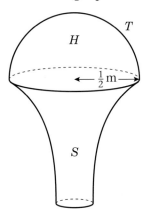

A sporting trophy T is a uniform solid hemisphere H joined to the solid S. The hemisphere has radius $\frac{1}{2}$ m and its plane face coincides with the larger plane face of S, as shown above. Both H and S are made of the same material.

b Find the distance of the centre of mass of T from its plane face. **E**

45

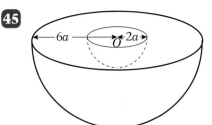

A uniform solid hemisphere, of radius $6a$ and centre O, has a solid hemisphere of radius $2a$, and centre O, removed to form a bowl B as shown above.

a Show that the centre of mass of B is $\frac{30}{13}a$ from O.

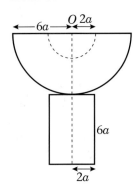

The bowl B is fixed to a plane face of a uniform solid cylinder made from the same material as B. The cylinder has radius $2a$ and height $6a$ and the combined solid S has an axis of symmetry which passes through O, as shown.

b Show that the centre of mass of S is $\frac{201}{61}a$ from O.

The plane surface of the cylindrical base of S is placed on a rough plane inclined at 12° to the horizontal. The plane is sufficiently rough to prevent slipping.

c Determine whether or not S will topple. **E**

46

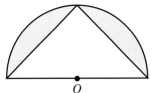

The diagram shows a cross section of a solid formed by the removal of a right circular cone, of base radius a and height a, from a uniform solid hemisphere of base radius a. The plane bases of the cone and the hemisphere are coincident, both having centre O. Show that G, the centre of mass of the solid, is at a distance $\frac{a}{2}$ from O.

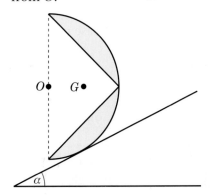

The second diagram shows a cross section of the solid resting in equilibrium with a point of its curved surface in contact with a rough inclined plane of inclination α. Given that O and G are in the same vertical plane through a line of greatest slope of the inclined plane, and that OG is horizontal, show that $\alpha = \frac{\pi}{6}$.

Given that $\alpha = \frac{\pi}{6}$, find the smallest possible value of the coefficient of friction between the solid and the plane. **E**

47

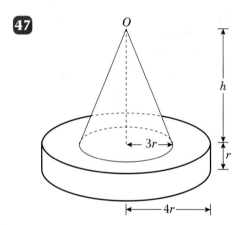

An experimental plastic traffic bollard B is made by joining a uniform solid cylinder to a uniform solid right circular cone of the same density. They are joined to form a symmetrical solid, in such a way that the centre of the plane face of the cone coincides with the centre of one of the plane faces of the cylinder, as shown in the diagram.

The cylinder has radius $4r$ and height r. The cone has vertex O, base radius $3r$ and height h.

a Show that the distance from O of the centre of mass of B is

$$\frac{32r^2 + 64rh + 9h^2}{4(16r + 3h)}$$

The bollard is placed on a rough plane which is inclined at an angle α to the horizontal. The circular base of B is in contact with the inclined plane. Given that $h = 4r$ and that B is on the point of toppling,

b find α, to the nearest degree. **E**

48 **a** Show, by integration, that the centre of mass of a uniform solid hemisphere, of radius R, is at a distance $\frac{3}{8}R$ from its plane face.

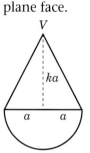

The diagram shows a uniform solid top made from a right circular cone of base radius a and height ka and a hemisphere of radius a. The circular plane faces of the cone and hemisphere are coincident.

b Show that the distance of the centre of mass of the top from the vertex V of the cone is

$$\frac{(3k^2 + 8k + 3)a}{4(k + 2)}$$

The manufacturer requires the top to have its centre of mass situated at the centre of the coincident plane faces.

c Find the value of k for this requirement. **E**

49 **a** A uniform solid hemisphere H has base radius a and the centre of its plane circular face is C.

The plane face of a second hemisphere K, of radius $\frac{a}{2}$, and made of the same material as H, is stuck to the plane face of H, so that the centres of the two plane faces coincide at C, to form a uniform composite body S. Given that the mass of K is M, show that the mass of S is $9M$, and find, in terms of a, the distance of the centre of mass of the body S from C.

b A particle P, of mass M, is attached to a point on the edge of the circular face of H of the body S. The body S with P

attached is placed with a point of the curved surface of the part H in contact with a horizontal plane and rests in equilibrium. Find the tangent of the acute angle made by the line PC with the horizontal. **E**

50 **a** Prove, by integration, that the position of the centre of mass of a uniform solid right circular cone is one quarter of the way up the axis from the base.

b From a uniform solid right circular cone of height H is removed a cone with the same base and height h, the two axes coinciding. Show that the centre of mass of the remaining solid S is a distance

$$\tfrac{1}{4}(3H - h)$$

from the vertex of the original cone.

c The solid S is suspended by two vertical strings, one attached to the vertex and the other attached to a point on the bounding circular base. Given that S is in equilibrium, with its axis of symmetry horizontal, find, in terms of H and h, the ratio of the magnitude of the tension in the string attached to the vertex to that in the other string. **E**

Examination style paper

1 A particle P moves along the positive x-axis such that when its displacement from the origin O is x metres, its velocity is $v\,\mathrm{m\,s^{-1}}$ and its acceleration is $(2 + x)\,\mathrm{m\,s^{-2}}$. When $x = 2$, $v = 4$.

   Show that $v = x + 2$. (5)

   (Total 5 marks)

2 A light elastic spring has natural length $0.6\,\mathrm{m}$ and modulus of elasticity $0.7\,\mathrm{N}$. The ends of the spring are attached to two fixed points, P and Q, where PQ is horizontal. A particle of mass $0.2\,\mathrm{kg}$ is attached to the mid-point of the spring and hangs at rest in equilibrium $0.6\,\mathrm{m}$ vertically below the mid-point of PQ, as shown in Figure 1.

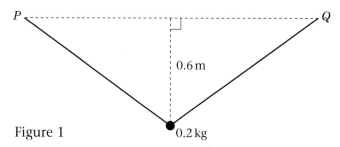

   Figure 1

   Find the length PQ. (9)

   (Total 9 marks)

3 In a harbour, sea level at low tide is $10\,\mathrm{m}$ below the level of the sea at high tide. At low tide the depth of the water in the harbour is $8\,\mathrm{m}$. On a particular day, low tide occurs at 1 p.m. and the next high tide occurs at 1.30 a.m. A ship can remain in the harbour safely when the depth of water is at least $12\,\mathrm{m}$. The sea level is modelled as rising and falling with simple harmonic motion.

   a Write down the period and amplitude of the motion. (2)

   b Find the length of time, on this particular day, for which it is safe for the ship to remain in the harbour. (7)

   (Total 9 marks)

4 The region R is bounded by the curve with equation $y = \sqrt{\cos 2x}$, the positive x-axis and the positive y-axis. The unit of length on both axes is $1\,\mathrm{m}$. A uniform solid S is formed by rotating R through 2π about the x-axis.

   a Show that the volume of S is $\dfrac{\pi}{2}\,\mathrm{m^3}$. (4)

b Find, in terms π, the x-coordinate of the centre of mass of S. (7)

The solid S is placed on an inclined plane, rough enough to prevent slipping, with its circular face on the plane. The plane is slowly tilted until the solid S is about to topple.

c Find the inclination of the plane to the horizontal when the solid S is about to topple. (4)

(Total 15 marks)

5 A circular track is banked at an angle α to the horizontal, where $\tan \alpha = \frac{3}{4}$. A car moves round the track at constant speed in a horizontal circle of radius 30 m. The car is modelled as a particle and the track is modelled as being smooth and any non-gravitational resistance to motion is ignored.

a Find the speed of the car. (6)

The model is now refined to allow for the roughness of the track and the coefficient of friction between the car and the track is taken as 0.5. Any non-gravitational resistance to motion is still ignored.

b Using this new model, find the maximum speed at which the car can move round the track on the same path without skidding off the track. (8)

(Total 14 marks)

6 A particle P of mass m is attached to one end of a light inextensible string of length a. The other end of the string is attached to a fixed point O. The particle is held with the string taut so that OP makes an angle of $60°$ with the downward vertical. The particle is then projected with speed $\sqrt{3ga}$ in a direction which is perpendicular to OP.

a Show that P does not make complete circles about O. (5)

b Find the angle that OP makes with the upward vertical when the string first goes slack. (9)

(Total 14 marks)

7 A light elastic string has natural length a and modulus of elasticity $3mg$. One end of the string is attached to a fixed point A. The other end is attached to a particle P of mass m. The particle is held at A and projected vertically downwards with speed $\sqrt{6ag}$. Ignoring air resistance, find the distance that P travels before it first comes to instantaneous rest. (9)

(Total 9 marks)

Answers

Exercise 1A

1 $(16 - 12e^{-0.25t}) \, \text{m s}^{-1}$

3 $2\ln 3 \, \text{m}$

4 11.5 (3 s.f.)

5 **a** $6\sqrt{2} \, \text{m s}^{-2}$ **b** $x = \frac{4}{3}\sin 3t$ **c** $t = \frac{\pi}{3}$

6 $v = \frac{3}{2} - \frac{3}{2 + t^2}$

7 **a**

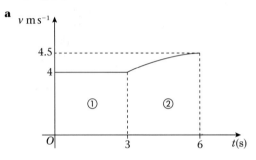

   b $(27 - 3\ln 2) \, \text{m}$

8 **a** $4 \, \text{m s}^{-1}$ **b** $(\pi - 2\sqrt{2}) \, \text{m}$

9 **a** $v = 40 - 20\,e^{0.2t}$ **b** $200\ln 2 - 100$

10 **a** $c = 80, d = 1$ **b** $3200\ln\left(\dfrac{80 + t}{80}\right)$

11 **a** $t = \ln 2.5, \ln 3$ **b** $\left(18 - \dfrac{15(\ln 3)^2}{2}\right) \text{m}$

12 **a** $t = 3$ **b** $(12 + 3\ln 12) \, \text{m}$

Exercise 1B

1 $v^2 = \dfrac{x^2}{2} + 4x + 25$

2 $v = \pm\sqrt{(80 - 4x^2)}$

3 $\frac{1}{5}$

4 $16 \, \text{m}$

5 **a** $\frac{6}{125}$

   b $\pm 4\sqrt{14} \, \text{m s}^{-1}$ as the particle will pass through this position in both directions.

6 4

7 **a** $v^2 = 52 - 36\cos\dfrac{x}{3}$

   b $2\sqrt{22} \, \text{m s}^{-1} \, (\approx 9.38 \, \text{m s}^{-1})$

8 $4.66 \, \text{m s}^{-1}$ (3 s.f.), in the direction of x increasing.

9 **a** $1.95 \, \text{m s}^{-1}$ (3 s.f.)   **b** 26.8 (3 s.f.)

10 **a** $v = x + \dfrac{2}{x}$ **b** $2\sqrt{2} \, \text{m s}^{-1}$

11 $10 \, \text{m}$

12 **a** $v = 3x^{\frac{2}{3}}$ **b** $x = (t + 2)^3$

Mixed exercise 1C

1 $\sqrt{\left(20 - \dfrac{12}{x}\right)}$

2 **a** $8(e^{0.5t} - 1)$ **b** $6 \, \text{m s}^{-2}$

3 $x = 8$

4 $x = \frac{1}{5}$

5 **a** $v = 18 - 10e^{-t^2}$ **b** $18 \, \text{m s}^{-1}$

6 6

7 **a** $v^2 = 16 + 6x - x^2$ **b** 5

8 **a** $v^2 = \dfrac{5x^3}{3} - \dfrac{x^4}{4} + \dfrac{2500}{3}$

   b $\dfrac{50\sqrt{3}}{3} \, \text{m s}^{-1}$

9 **a** $6.04 \, \text{m s}^{-1}$ (3 s.f.)   **b** 2.56 (3 s.f.)

10 **a** $v = 10 - \dfrac{50}{2t + 5}$

   b $(100 - 25\ln 5) \, \text{m} \approx 59.8 \, \text{m}$

11 **a** $\dfrac{\pi}{2} \, \text{m s}^{-1}$ **b** $\frac{1}{64}(\pi^2 + 8) \, \text{m}$

12 **a** $2.5 \, \text{m s}^{-2}$ in the direction of x increasing.

   b $8\,e^{-1} \, \text{m s}^{-2}$ in the direction of x decreasing.

   c $\left(\dfrac{56}{3} - 8\,e^{-2}\right) \text{m} \approx 17.6 \, \text{m}$ (3 s.f.)

13 **a** $7 \, \text{m s}^{-1}$ **b** $x = 7.6$ (2 s.f.)

14 **a** $v = 2t + \ln(t + 1)$ **b** $(2 + 3\ln 3) \, \text{m}$

15 **a** $v = 2x + 3$ **b** $x = \frac{3}{2}(e^{2t} - 1)$

Exercise 2A

1 **a** $3.4 \, \text{m}$ **b** $4 \, \text{m}$ **c** $3.75 \, \text{m}$

2 $4 \, \text{m}$

3 $1.31 \, \text{m}$ (3 s.f.)

4 $\dfrac{mga}{\lambda}$

5 $l = \dfrac{m_1 a_2 - m_2 a_1}{m_1 - m_2}$

   $g\dfrac{(m_1 a_2 - m_2 a_1)}{(a_1 - a_2)}$

6 $\dfrac{11a}{4}$

7 **a** $14.7 \, \text{N}$ **b** $2.7 \, \text{m}$ (2 s.f.)

8 $\dfrac{11l}{4}$

9 **a** $1 \, \text{m}$ **b** $0.58 \, \text{m}$ (2 s.f.)

   c $17 \, \text{N}$ (2 s.f.)

10 **a** $3.9 \, \text{N}$ (2 s.f.)   **b** $0.96 \, \text{m}$ (2 s.f.)

Exercise 2B

1 **a** $6 \, \text{m s}^{-2}$ **b** $2 \, \text{m s}^{-2}$

2 $12.5 \, \text{m s}^{-2}$

3 $14.2 \, \text{m s}^{-2}$ upwards

4 $3.13 \, \text{m s}^{-2}$ downwards

Exercise 2C

1 1.07 J
2 0.1 J
3 1.125 J
4 **a** 0.571 J   **b** 1.14 J   **c** 3.43 J
5 23 J (2 s.f.)
6 $2mga$

Exercise 2D

1 $V = \frac{1}{2}\sqrt{gl}$

2 $\frac{3a}{4} = d$

3 Modulus is $mg\sqrt{3}$

4 **a** $V = 2\,\text{m s}^{-1}$ **b** 0.80 m (2 s.f.)

5 $U = \sqrt{\frac{3ag}{2}}$

6 **a** 160 N (2 s.f.)   **b** 2.9 m s^{-1} (2 s.f.)
7 **a** Falls 4 m   **b** 6.6 m s^{-1} (2 s.f.)
8 0.11 (2 s.f.)

Mixed exercise 2E

1 **b** $\frac{11mga}{12}$

2 $3a$
3 **a** $\lambda = 30\,\text{N}$ **b** $v = 2.19\,\text{m s}^{-1}$ (3 s.f.)

4 $l = \frac{5\lambda a}{(5\lambda + 3mg)}$

5 **a** $V = \sqrt{\frac{13ag}{20}}$ **b** $d = \frac{13a}{50}$

6 **a** $\frac{\lambda x^2}{2l}$

7 **a** $\mu = \frac{2}{3}$ **b** $V = \sqrt{\frac{2gl}{3}}$ **c** $\frac{3l}{2}$

8 **a** $\frac{4\cos\theta - 3}{4\sin\theta - 1}$

9 **a** $\theta = \tan^{-1}\left(\frac{1}{3}\right)$ **b** 2.1 m (2 s.f.)   **c** 9.3 N (2 s.f.)

10 **a** $v = 2\sqrt{ga}$ **b** $T = mg$

Exercise 3A

1 **a** 9.09 m s^{-1} (3 s.f.)   **b** 1.41 m s^{-1} (3 s.f.)
   c P first comes to rest when $t = \pi$
   d 14.2 m (3 s.f.)   **e** $OP = 20\,\text{m}$
2 **a** 10
   b The van moves 10.6 m in the first 4 seconds (3 s.f.)
3 **a** $x = 15$ **b** 9.86 m s^{-1} (3 s.f.)
4 **a** 6.79 m s^{-1} (3 s.f.)   **b** 8.23 m s^{-1} (3 s.f.)
5 $x = 0.314$ (3 s.f.)
6 **a** 60 Ns   **b** 3.46 Ns (3 s.f.)
   c 0 Ns   **d** 13.7 Ns (3 s.f.)

7 **a** $19\frac{5}{6}$ J (or 19.8 J (3 s.f.))

   b $\left(\frac{3\pi}{2} + 2\right)$ J or 6.71 J (3 s.f.)

   c 26.2 J (3 s.f.)
   d ln 72 J or 4.28 J (3 s.f.)
8 **a** 46.5 Ns   **b** 25 m s^{-1}
   c $T = 6.39$ (3 s.f.)
9 **a** $F = 0.12\,(x^2 + 2x)$
   b 4.48 J

Exercise 3B

3 $\sqrt{2gR}$

4 $\sqrt{\left[\dfrac{U^2X + U^2R - 2gRX}{(X + R)}\right]}$

5 $\sqrt{\dfrac{7gR}{5}}$

6 $2\sqrt{\dfrac{gR}{3}}$

Exercise 3C

1 **a** $\frac{\pi}{2}$ s   **b** 1.83 m s^{-1} (3 s.f.)

2 **a** 1 m   **b** 1.36 m s^{-1} (3 s.f.)
3 **a** 5 m   **b** π s

4 $\frac{4}{3}$ m s^{-1}

5 17.9 m s^{-1} (3 s.f.)
6 **a** 1.26 m (3 s.f.)   **b** $x = 1.26\sin 4t$
7 **a** 0.133 m (3 s.f.)   **b** 0.0141 m (3 s.f.)
8 **a** 1.37 m (3 s.f.)   **b** 0.684 s (3 s.f.)
9 **a** 1.00 m s^{-1} (3 s.f.)   **b** 0.922 m s^{-1} (3 s.f.)
10 9.25 J (3 s.f.)
11 **a** 1.26 m s^{-1} (3 s.f.)   **b** $\frac{2}{3}$ s to fall 0.6 m
12 0.0738 s (3 s.f.)

13 **b** 4, $\frac{2\pi}{2} = \pi$ s   **c** 8 m s^{-1}

   d $\frac{\pi}{6}$ **e** $\frac{\pi}{12}$

14 **b** Amplitude = 3 m

   Period = $\frac{\pi}{2}$ s

   c $x = 1.44$ (3 s.f.)
   d 0.660 (3 s.f.)
15 **a** 11.51 a.m. (nearest minute)
   b 8.39 p.m. (nearest minute)
16 P takes 0.823 s to travel directly from B to A (3 s.f.)

Exercise 3D

1 **b** $\frac{\pi}{10}\sqrt{2}$ s   0.3 m   **c** 4.24 m s^{-1} (3 s.f.)

2 **b** 3.21 s (3 s.f.)
3 **b** 0.489 s (3 s.f.)   **c** 1.84 m (3 s.f.)
4 **b** Period is 0.688 s (3 s.f.)
   Amplitude is $1.2 - 0.6 = 0.6$ m
   c 5.48 m s^{-1} (3 s.f.)
5 **a** $x = 0.5\sin 10t$
   b 50 m s^{-2}
6 **a** 0.5 m   **b** 2.11 m s^{-1} (3 s.f.)
   c i 1.49 s   **ii** 0.300 m (3 s.f.)
7 **a** 0.351 s (3 s.f.)   **b** 2.56 J
8 **a** 2.45 m s^{-1} (3 s.f.)   **b** 1.17 (3 s.f.)
9 **b** 3.6 J

10 **b** $2\pi\sqrt{\dfrac{l}{6g}}$ **c** 1.5l

   d $\sqrt{12gl}$ (or $2\sqrt{3gl}$)

11 **b** 1 m

Exercise 3E

1 a 1.64 m (3 s.f.)   **c** 0.745 s (3 s.f.)
   d 0.296 m (3 s.f.)
2 a 0.049 m (or 4.9 cm)

   b $\frac{\pi}{10}\sqrt{2}$ s (or 0.444 s (3 s.f.))

   c $2\sqrt{2}$ m s^{-1} (or 2.83 m s^{-1} (3 s.f.))
3 a 1.5 m s^{-1} **c** 48   **d** 0.375 m
4 b 0.2 m   **c** 2 m s^{-1} **d** 20 m s^{-2}
5 a 0.138 s (3 s.f.)   **b** 0.0353 m s^{-1} (3 s.f.)
6 a 31.4 N (3 s.f.)   **c** 0.449 s, 0.07 m
   d 0.98 m s^{-1}
   e 0.156 s to rise 11 cm (3 s.f.)
7 a 0.416 s (3 s.f.)   **b** 0.0574 s (3 s.f.)
8 a 0.221 m   **b** 0.517 s (3 s.f.)
9 a 1.69 m (3 s.f.)   **c** 0.398 (3 s.f.)
10 a 12.5 m s^{-1} (3 s.f.)   **b** 10.4 m (3 s.f.)
   c 1.56 s (3 s.f.)

Mixed exercise 3F

1 a $\frac{4\pi}{50}$ (or 0.251 (3 s.f.)) **b** 0.203 m s^{-1} (3 s.f.)
   c 0.318 m (3 s.f.)
2 a $x = 2.5$ **b** $v^2 = 25x - 5x^2 + 32.75$
3 a 108   **b** 11.8 m (3 s.f.)
4 b Amplitude = 3 m
      Period = 8 s

   c $\frac{3\pi}{4}$ m s^{-1} (or 2.36 m s^{-1} (3 s.f.))

   d 0.405 s (3 s.f.)
5 a $\lambda = 3\,g$ **c** 0.898 s (3 s.f.)
   d 2.01 m s^{-1} (3 s.f.)   **e** 0.406 m (3 s.f.)

6 b $\sqrt{\left(\frac{8Rg}{5}\right)}$ or $2\sqrt{\left(\frac{2Rg}{5}\right)}$

7 b $2\pi\sqrt{\left(\frac{l}{5g}\right)}$ **c** $\frac{3}{4}\sqrt{5gl}$

8 a $\dot{x} = \frac{-20}{3}(3t + 4)^{\frac{1}{2}} + \frac{76}{3}$

   b 18.7 m from O (3 s.f.)
9 b Period is 1.54 s (3 s.f.)
      Amplitude is $(4 - 2.5)$ m = 1.5 m
   c P takes 0.468 s to move 2 m from B (3 s.f.)
10 b 1.38 s (3 s.f.)
   c 0.229 s to reach D (3 s.f.)

Review Exercise 1

2 $v^2 = 4x^2$
3 a $v = 13 - 3e^{-\frac{1}{6}t}$ **b** 11.2 m s^{-1} (3 s.f.)
   c 13
5 8.76 m s^{-1} (3 s.f.)

6 a $4k^2\left(1 - \frac{2}{x + 1}\right)$

7 a $x = 30$ **b** $v^2 = 5x - \frac{x^2}{12} + 25$
8 a $v = 8 - 4\cos\frac{1}{2}t$ **b** $4(\pi - \sqrt{2})$ m
9 a $v = 2e^{-2t} - 1$ **b** $\frac{1}{2}(1 - \ln 2)$ m
10 b 162 m
11 a 0.9 m   **c** 1 m

12 a

   b $2 < t < 5$ **c** 39 m   **d** 6.98 (3 s.f.)
13 a $v^2 = 60 - \frac{72}{2x + 1}$ **b** 0.1 m
15 b $p = \frac{1}{20}, q = \frac{3}{1600}$ **c** $x = \frac{1600}{3}\ln\left(1 + \frac{3}{80}t\right)$
16 11 m s^{-1} (2 s.f.)
17 a $5Mg$ **c** $20Mg$
18 42
19 b 4.8   **c** 13.2 N
20 a $\frac{l}{4}$
21 a The line of action of the weight must pass through C which is not above the centre of the rod.
   b $\frac{6}{5}mg$ **c** $k = 8$
22 a 14 (2 s.f.)   **b** 0.78 m (2 s.f.)
   c 6.1 J (2 s.f.)
23 $3mg$
24 a $0.2mga$ **b** 0.6
25 $\frac{3}{4}a$
26 a 4 m
   b 29.4 m s^{-2} directed towards A
27 a 2.89 m s^{-1} (3 s.f.)   **b** 7.79 N (3 s.f.)
28 a $\frac{4a}{3}$ **b** $4\left(\frac{ga}{3}\right)^{\frac{1}{2}}$
29 a 105 N   **b** 140 N   **c** 42 J
30 a $\frac{49}{36}mga$ **b** $\frac{2}{3}\sqrt{(5ga)}$
31 a 6 m   **b** 14 m s^{-1} (2 s.f.)
32 a 1.8 m s^{-1} (2 s.f.)
34 a $2\sqrt{(gl)}$ **b** $\sqrt{(7gl)}$ **c** $\left(\frac{145gl}{8}\right)^{\frac{1}{2}}$
35 53.6 (3 s.f.)
36 a $v^2 = 20 - 16e^{-0.1x}$ **b** $x = 10\ln 4$
37 a $v^2 = 2x^2 - x^3 + 144$ **b** 12 m s^{-1}
38 a $t = -2\ln\left(\frac{2}{5}\right)$ or $2\ln\left(\frac{5}{2}\right)$
   b $(4 + 20e^{-1})$ m
39 a 3.78 m s^{-1} (3 s.f.)   **b** 3.83 m (3 s.f.)
40 b $\sqrt{\left(\frac{gR}{6}\right)}$
41 b $\frac{1}{2}RU^2$
42 b $X = \frac{2gR^2}{2gR - U^2}$
43 a 30 m s^{-1} **b** $(180 - 120\ln 2)$ m
44 a 6   **b** 17 m
45 $\frac{2}{3}$
46 a 19.7 N (3 s.f.)   **b** 5.44 m s^{-1} (3 s.f.)
47 a 1.3 m   **b** 2.6 m s^{-1}

c $5.2\,\text{m}\,\text{s}^{-2}$ **d** $0.79\,\text{s}$ (2 d.p.)

48 b $v = \dfrac{\sqrt{2}\,\pi L}{3}$ **c** $0.28\,\text{s}$ (2 d.p.)

49 c $0.15\,\text{m}\,\text{s}^{-2}$ **d** $0.412\,\text{s}$ (3 s.f.)

50 a $\dfrac{\pi}{4}\,\text{m}\,\text{h}^{-1}$ **b** 4 hours

51 b $6\,\text{m}\,\text{s}^{-1}$ **c** $\dfrac{\pi}{15}\,\text{s}$

52 b $6.25\,\text{m}\,\text{s}^{-2}$ **c** $0.68\,\text{m}\,\text{s}^{-1}$ (2 s.f.)
    d As it passes through C, P is moving away from O towards B.

53 b $4mg$ **c** $\frac{1}{2}\sqrt{(3gl)}$
    d First P moves freely under gravity until it returns to B. Then it moves with simple harmonic motion about O.

54 a $\dfrac{9a}{2}$ **c** $\dfrac{1}{2\sqrt{2}}a$
    d As $a > \frac{1}{2}a$, the string will become slack during its motion. The subsequent motion of P will be partly under gravity, partly simple harmonic motion.

55 b $9\,\text{m}\,\text{s}^{-1}$ **c** $\dfrac{\pi}{18}\,\text{s}$
    d $1.16\,\text{m}$ (3 s.f.)

56 c The maximum magnitude of the acceleration is g.
    d $\dfrac{\pi}{12}\sqrt{\left(\dfrac{a}{g}\right)}$

Exercise 4A

1 a $0.524\,\text{rad}\,\text{s}^{-1}$ **b** $12.6\,\text{rad}\,\text{s}^{-1}$
    c $38.2\,\text{rev}\,\text{min}^{-1}$ **d** $1720\,\text{rev}\,\text{h}^{-1}$

2 a $80\,\text{m}\,\text{s}^{-1}$ **b** $83.8\,\text{m}\,\text{s}^{-1}$

3 a $8\,\text{rad}\,\text{s}^{-1}$ **b** $76.4\,\text{rev}\,\text{min}^{-1}$

4 a $2\,\text{m}\,\text{s}^{-1}$ **b** $2.09\,\text{m}\,\text{s}^{-1}$

5 a $44.9\,\text{s}$ **b** $0.14\,\text{rad}\,\text{s}^{-1}$

6 a $0.628\,\text{rad}\,\text{s}^{-1}$ **b** $0.0754\,\text{m}\,\text{s}^{-1}$
    c $0.0503\,\text{m}\,\text{s}^{-1}$

7 a $0.279\,\text{rad}\,\text{s}^{-1}$ **b** $39.8\,\text{m}$

8 $3.14\,\text{m}\,\text{s}^{-1}$, $5.24\,\text{m}\,\text{s}^{-1}$

9 a $0.242\,\text{rad}\,\text{s}^{-1}$ **b** $0.362\,\text{m}\,\text{s}^{-1}$

10 $0.056\,\text{rad}\,\text{s}^{-1}$

11 a $0.000145\,\text{rad}\,\text{s}^{-1}$, $0.00175\,\text{rad}\,\text{s}^{-1}$
    b $1.45 \times 10^{-5}\,\text{m}\,\text{s}^{-1}$, $2.62 \times 10^{-4}\,\text{m}\,\text{s}^{-1}$

12 $62.8\,\text{m}\,\text{s}^{-1}$

13 a $4.71\,\text{rad}\,\text{s}^{-1}$ **b** 2.55

14 $30\,000\,\text{m}\,\text{s}^{-1}$

Exercise 4B

1 $4\,\text{m}\,\text{s}^{-2}$

2 $20.8\,\text{m}\,\text{s}^{-2}$

3 a $5\,\text{rad}\,\text{s}^{-1}$ **b** $15\,\text{m}\,\text{s}^{-1}$

4 a $12.9\,\text{rad}\,\text{s}^{-1}$ **b** $7.75\,\text{m}\,\text{s}^{-1}$

5 $2.14\,\text{m}\,\text{s}^{-2}$

6 $0.283\,\text{rad}\,\text{s}^{-1}$

7 $0.72\,\text{N}$

8 $48.6\,\text{N}$

9 a $0.59\,\text{N}$ **b** $4.5\,\text{N}$

10 a $0.24\,\text{m}\,\text{s}^{-1}$ **b** $0.0072\,\text{N}$

11 0.029

12 $3.1\,\text{rad}\,\text{s}^{-1}$

13 0.16

14 $0.23\,\text{rad}\,\text{s}^{-1}$

15 $0.322\,\text{m}$

16 $320\,\text{N}$

17 $2.42\,\text{rad}\,\text{s}^{-1}$

18 $1.4\,\text{m}\,\text{s}^{-1}$

Exercise 4C

1 $18\,\text{N}$, $4.5\,\text{rad}\,\text{s}^{-1}$

2 $10\,\text{N}$, $4.4\,\text{rad}\,\text{s}^{-1}$

3 $23.7\,\text{N}$, $60°$

4 $73.5\,\text{N}$, $0.6\,\text{m}$

5 $T = ml\omega^2$

7 $R = 3mg$, $\omega = \sqrt{\dfrac{3g}{r}}$

8 $\omega = \sqrt{\dfrac{g}{3}}$

9 $5\,\text{cm}$

10 $9.5°$

11 $23\,\text{m}\,\text{s}^{-1}$

12 $9.44\,\text{m}\,\text{s}^{-1}$

14 $2.21\,\text{m}\,\text{s}^{-1}$

15 0.40

16 $42°$

17 $29.5\,\text{m}\,\text{s}^{-1}$, $9.9\,\text{m}\,\text{s}^{-1}$

18 $13.4\,\text{N}$, $7.8\,\text{rad}\,\text{s}^{-1}$

19 $2.2\,\text{rad}\,\text{s}^{-1}$

20 $20°$, $21\,000\,\text{N}$; $68°$, $53\,000\,\text{N}$

Exercise 4D

1 a i $v = -r\omega \sin \omega t\,\mathbf{i} + r\omega \cos \omega t\,\mathbf{j}$

2 a $\mathbf{r}$ is perpendicular to v.
    b The direction of the velocity at any instant is along the tangent to the circular path.

3 a $a = -\omega^2(r\cos \omega t\,\mathbf{i} + r\sin \omega t\,\mathbf{j})$
    b $a = -\omega^2\mathbf{r}$
    The direction of the acceleration is towards the centre of the circle.
    c $a = r\omega^2$

Exercise 4E

1 a $3.1\,\text{m}\,\text{s}^{-1}$ **b** $17.6\,\text{N}$

2 a $3.4\,\text{m}\,\text{s}^{-1}$ **b** $19.6\,\text{N}$

3 a $3.0\,\text{m}\,\text{s}^{-1}$ **b** $15.7\,\text{N}$

4 a $2.2\,\text{m}\,\text{s}^{-1}$ **b** $5.9\,\text{N}$

5 a $8.5\,\text{m}\,\text{s}^{-1}$ **b** $46.9\,\text{N}$

6 a $v^2 = u^2 - 1.4g(1 - \cos \theta)$
    b $u > \sqrt{2.8g}$

7 a $T = 4.5g \cos \theta + \dfrac{3u^2}{4} - 3g$
    b $u > \sqrt{10g}$

8 a 0.27 **b** 0.26

9 a 0.30 **b** 0.28

10 a $6.3\,\text{m}\,\text{s}^{-1}$, $23\,\text{N}$ **b** $5.6\,\text{m}\,\text{s}^{-1}$, $19\,\text{N}$

11 a $9.7\,\text{m}\,\text{s}^{-1}$ **b** $g\,\text{m}\,\text{s}^{-2}$ **c** $45.8\,\text{N}$

12 $40°$ to the upward vertical, $2.7°$

13 $\sqrt{8gr}$

14 a $\sqrt{\dfrac{16gr}{5}}$ **b** $\dfrac{11mg}{5}$

15 a $T = mg(1 + 3\sin \theta)$
    b $19.5°$

Exercise 4F

1 a $mg + 3mg \cos \theta$ b $\dfrac{4l}{3}$ c $\dfrac{40l}{27}$

2 a $9g \cos \theta - 6g$ b $48°$ c $6.7\,m$

3 a $\dfrac{9rg}{4} - 2rg \cos \theta$ b $\dfrac{3}{4}$ c $\sqrt{\dfrac{3rg}{4}}$

  d $\dfrac{3\sqrt{rg}}{2}$ e $64°$

4 a $48°$ b $\sqrt{8g}, 74°$

5 a $\dfrac{a}{4}$ b $\sqrt{\dfrac{ga}{4}}$ c $64°$

6 $49°$

7 a $10.3\,m\,s^{-1}$ b Not in contact.

8 $\sqrt{\dfrac{17ga}{3}}$

Mixed exercise 4G

2 a $\dfrac{3mg}{2}$ b $\dfrac{mg}{2}$

3 a $\dfrac{13mg}{5}$ b $\sqrt{60gl}$

4 $108\,m$

5 b $\dfrac{m}{2}(l\omega^2 - 2g)$

6 a $\sqrt{\dfrac{\sqrt{2g}}{l}}$

7 b $\dfrac{5g}{42a} \leqslant \omega^2 \leqslant \dfrac{65g}{42a}$

8 a $6.48\,N$ b $25°$

9 a $4mg$ b $3\pi\sqrt{\dfrac{r}{g}}$

10 a $\dfrac{4}{3}ga + 2ga \sin \theta$ b $mg\left(\dfrac{4}{3} + 3 \sin \theta\right)$

   c $206°$

   d $v = 0$ before the particle reaches the top of the circle.

11 $\sqrt{2.6g}$

12 a $\dfrac{ga}{2}(5 - 4 \cos \theta)$ c i $\dfrac{5}{6}$ ii $\sqrt{\dfrac{5ga}{6}}$

   d $\sqrt{\dfrac{5ga}{2}}$ e $61°$

13 a $u^2 - \dfrac{16}{5}gr$ b $\dfrac{mg}{5}$

   c $\sqrt{\dfrac{19gr}{5}}$ d $\sqrt{\dfrac{73gr}{15}}$

14 a $\dfrac{u^2 + 2ag}{3ag}$ b $34°$

Exercise 5A

1 $\left(\dfrac{2}{3}, 2\right)$

2 $(1.5, 3.6)$

3 $(2.4, 0.75)$

4 $\left(\dfrac{14}{25}, \dfrac{23}{35}\right)$

5 $\left(\dfrac{3}{5}a, 0\right)$

6 $\left(\dfrac{\pi}{2}, \dfrac{\pi}{8}\right)$

7 $\left(\dfrac{1 - \ln 2}{\ln 2}, \dfrac{1}{4 \ln 2}\right)$

8 $\left(\dfrac{4\sqrt{2}\,r}{3\pi}, 0\right)$

9 $\left(\dfrac{16}{15}, \dfrac{64}{21}\right)$

10 The centre of mass is on the axis of symmetry at a distance $\dfrac{52}{15\pi}$ above the common diameter.

11 $1.2\,cm$ (2 s.f.)

12 $\left(2\dfrac{54}{55}, 1\dfrac{5}{11}\right)$

Exercise 5B

1 $(2, 0)$

2 $(1, 0)$

3 $(\pi, 0)$

4 $(0, -3)$

5 $\left(\dfrac{5}{6}, 0\right)$

6 $\left(2\dfrac{2}{3}, 0\right)$

7 $\left(\dfrac{35}{48}, 0\right)$

8 $(1.65, 0)$ (3 s.f.)

9 $\left(\dfrac{1}{2}\dfrac{(e^2 + 1)}{(e^2 - 1)}, 0\right)$

10 $\left(\dfrac{e^4 - 5}{2(e^4 - 1)}, 0\right)$

11 a The centre of mass lies on the axis of symmetry at a point $\dfrac{5}{16}\,cm$ from O towards the vertex of the cone.

   b The centre of mass lies on the axis of symmetry at a point $\dfrac{5}{12}\,cm$ from O away from the vertex of the cone.

12 a Centre of mass is on the axis of symmetry at a distance $2\dfrac{13}{14}\,cm$ away from base of hemisphere.

   b Centre of mass is on the axis of symmetry at a distance $1\dfrac{1}{22}\,cm$ away from the base of the hemisphere.

13 $1\dfrac{6}{13}$ or 1.46 (3 s.f.)

14 a $3.14\,cm$
   b $3.04\,cm$

15 $\dfrac{r}{3}$ above the base

16 $\dfrac{5}{6}\,cm$ above the base

17 $1.05\,cm$

18 $\dfrac{h(4a - h)}{4(3a - h)}$

19 $\dfrac{R}{2}$ from the plane face

Exercise 5C

1 $\theta = 68°$ (to the nearest degree)

2 $\theta = 40°$ (to the nearest degree)

3 $\theta = 63°$ (to the nearest degree)

4 a $2.78\,cm$ from large circular face
   b $\alpha = 51°$ (to the nearest degree)

5 $\tan \alpha \leqslant \dfrac{1}{2}$ (i.e. $k = \dfrac{1}{2}$)

6 $\tan \alpha \leqslant \dfrac{3}{4}$ (i.e. $k = \dfrac{3}{4}$)

7 $\alpha = 22°$ (to the nearest degree)

8 $30°$

9 a $\dfrac{29r}{32}$

10 $h = \dfrac{r\sqrt{2}}{2}$

13 b $T = \dfrac{\sqrt{5}\,mg}{2}$

Exercise 5D

1 4.77 cm (3 s.f.)

2 a 31° (to the nearest degree)

   b $\mu \geqslant \frac{3}{5}$

3 a 30°   **b** 35 cm (2 s.f.)

4 a $\dfrac{2Mg}{2 + \sqrt{3}}$ **b** $\frac{1}{2}$

5 b i Yes   **ii** No

   c $\mu \geqslant 0.839$ (3 s.f.)

6 b $2a$

7 a $\frac{7}{4}h$

8 b $\alpha = 29°$ (to the nearest degree

   c $\mu > \frac{44}{81}$

9 b $\theta = 38°$ (to the nearest degree)

10 b i fall over   **ii** return to vertical position

    iii remain in new position

Mixed exercise 5E

1 b $\bar{x} = \frac{8}{3}$

2 b 39 cm to the nearest cm.

3 34 cm

4 $\dfrac{9r}{10}$

5 0.71 (2 s.f.)

   The centre of mass of the body is at C which is always directly above the contact point.

6 b $\theta = 79°$ (to the nearest degree)

7 c The distance from OC is a

   The distance from OB is $\dfrac{2a}{\pi}$

   d 78° (to the nearest degree)

8 b $\theta = 9°$ (to the nearest degree)

9 c $\rho_1 : \rho_2 = 6 : 1$

   d As centre of mass is at centre of hemisphere this will always be above the point of contact with the plane. (Tangent–radius property).

10 b $\theta = 38°$ (to the nearest degree)

Review Exercise 2

1 3.67 m s^{-1} (3 s.f.)

2 b $\omega = \sqrt{\dfrac{2g}{L}}$

3 190 (2 s.f.)

4 24 m s^{-1} (2 s.f.)

5 a $\dfrac{5mg}{4}$ **b** $v = \sqrt{6gl}$

   c The tensions could not be assumed to have the same magnitude.

6 a $\alpha = 70.5°$ **b** $l = \dfrac{3}{2k}$

7 a $T = 5.5$ N (2 s.f.)   **b** $\theta = 26°$ (nearest degree)

8 a $2mg$ **b** $2\pi\sqrt{\dfrac{r}{2g}}$

9 b $mg + \frac{1}{2}mh\omega^2$ and $\frac{1}{2}mh\omega^2 - mg$

10 c $T = \dfrac{2\sqrt{3}}{3}mg$ or $1.15mg$

11 $2a$

12 b $mg\left(1 - \dfrac{k}{3}\right)$ **c** $k < 3$

13 b $\frac{1}{6}m(3l\omega^2 - 4g)$

14 b $\omega_{max}^2 = \dfrac{19g}{20a}$ and $\omega_{min}^2 = \dfrac{g}{20a}$

15 a $u = \sqrt{\dfrac{gl}{2}}$ **b** $\dfrac{5l}{6}$

16 b $v = \sqrt{\dfrac{gl}{3}}$ **c** $\dfrac{40l}{27}$

17 a $\sqrt{\dfrac{2gl}{3}}$ **c** $\dfrac{2mg}{3} \leqslant T \leqslant \dfrac{5mg}{3}$

18 a $\frac{3}{4}$ or 0.75   **c** $u = 1.4$

19 b $\theta = 60°$ **c** $\left(\dfrac{7ga}{2}\right)^{\frac{1}{2}}$

20 a $\frac{3}{2}mg$ **c** $\sqrt{\dfrac{6a}{g}}$

21 a $v = 8$ **b** $m = 6$

   c $T = 132g$ or 1300 N (2 s.f.)

22 a 30 m s^{-1} **b** 1900 Newtons

   c 28 m s^{-1} **d** 560 N

   e Lower speed at $C \Rightarrow$ the normal reaction is reduced.

23 a $v^2 = ag(1 - 2\cos\theta)$ **c** $\frac{4}{3}a$

   d $\frac{4}{27}a$ or $0.148a$

24 a $\frac{3}{2}ga + 2ga\sin\theta$ **b** $\dfrac{3mg}{2}(1 + 2\sin\theta)$

   d Not a complete circle.

   f 73.2° (3 s.f.)

25 a $\dfrac{2}{3} + \dfrac{u^2}{3ag}$ **b** 34° (nearest degree)

26 a $u^2 - 3ga$ **b** $\dfrac{5mg}{2}$

   c $\sqrt{\dfrac{7ga}{2}}$ **d** $u = \sqrt{5ag}$

27 $\frac{8}{3}$ from O

28 a $\bar{x} = \dfrac{5r}{4}$ **b** $\theta = 47.5°$ (1 d.p.)

   c Toy will not topple.

29 a $\dfrac{51a}{64}$ or $0.797a$ (3 s.f.)

   b $\alpha = 70.6°$ **c** $\beta = 38.7°$

30 a $\dfrac{8\pi}{5}$ **c** $\dfrac{59W}{12}$

31 b $h = \sqrt{3}\,r$

32 b $r = \frac{1}{4}h$

33 b $\alpha = 72°$ (nearest degree)

34 b $\alpha = 66.5°$ (1 d.p.)

36 $\dfrac{2a}{\pi}$

37 b $\frac{8}{9}a$

39 b 76° (nearest degree)

40 56°

41 b $\frac{6}{7}r$

42 b $k = \frac{2}{7}$

43 $\theta = 53.1°$ (1 d.p.)

44 b $\frac{29}{30}$ m or 0.967 m

45 c S will not topple.

46 $\dfrac{1}{\sqrt{3}}$

47 b $\alpha = 74°$ (nearest degree)

48 b $v = \dfrac{\sqrt{2}\,\pi l}{3}$ **c** $k = \sqrt{3}$

49 a $\dfrac{5a}{16}$ **b** $\frac{16}{45}$

50 c $\dfrac{H + h}{3H - h}$

Examination style paper

1 $v = (x + 2)$

2 $1.6\,\text{m}$

3 b 14.1 hours

4 a $\dfrac{\pi}{2}$ **b** $\dfrac{\pi}{4} - \dfrac{1}{2}$ **c** $\alpha = 74°$

5 a $14.8\,\text{m}^{-1} = v$ **b** $24\,\text{m}^{-1}$ (2 s.f.)

6 a $v = 0$ at top   **b** $\theta = 48°$ (2 s.f.)

7 $3a$

Index